Elementary
Plasma Physics

A Blaisdell Book in the Pure and Applied Sciences

Bernard T. Feld, *Massachusetts Institute of Technology*

Elementary
Plasma Physics

LEV A. ARZIMOVICH
Academy of Sciences (U.S.S.R.)

TRANSLATED BY
Scripta Technica, Inc.

BLAISDELL PUBLISHING COMPANY
A Division of Ginn and Company
NEW YORK · TORONTO · LONDON

A translation of the original volume
Elementarnaya Fizika Plazmy
published by *Gosatomizdat*
(State Committee for Application of Atomic Energy
of the U.S.S.R., State Press for Atomic Physics
and Nuclear Engineering) Moscow, 1963

First English Edition, 1965

Preface

Plasma is a state of matter, normally found in extraterrestrial space. It possesses exceedingly interesting properties that are being increasingly applied to the solution of important problems of modern technology. Thus, the subject is of major interest to the general reader. However, the reader who desires an understanding of the basic properties of plasma encounters considerable difficulties. Most present-day books employ extremely complex mathematical tools and require a good preparation in modern theoretical physics. There is no need, however, to use complex mathematics to explain the basic phenomena occurring in plasma. Such mathematics is often misused and is consequently of no more than decorative significance.

We shall attempt to interpret the fundamentals of plasma physics in a manner understandable to a reader with a high-school knowledge of mathematics and physics. We do not mean to imply, however, that the material is presented in a predigested form — for assimilation without thought. Such an attitude is neither suitable nor possible in the study of plasma physics.

This book discusses not only the various plasma processes but also the methods of analysis of such processes. By becoming familiar with these methods, the reader will be able to attain a genuine understanding of the physical significance of the phenomena involved. The absolute cgs (centimeter, gram, second) system of units is used in all computations. In some cases, the practical system of electrical units (ampere, volt, joule) is also used.

Contents

Contents

Elementary
Plasma Physics

Introduction

1.1 Production of Plasma

Consider a closed vessel whose walls have a very high melting point and suppose that the vessel contains a small amount of a solid material. When the temperature of the vessel is gradually increased the solid will melt and eventually evaporate, filling the vessel uniformly with the resulting vapor. When the temperature is increased still further all the molecules of the gas will dissociate, that is, divide into individual atoms (if the gas was originally in molecular form such as hydrogen, nitrogen, or oxygen). The vessel will thus eventually contain a gaseous mixture of the elements corresponding to the original composition of the solid material. The atoms of these elements will be in a rapid and random motion as a result of which they will collide with each other. The average velocity of this random thermal motion is proportional to the square root of the temperature of the gas and inversely proportional to the square root of its atomic weight. The average thermal velocity v can be calculated from the following formula

$$v = 1.3 \times 10^4 \sqrt{\frac{T}{A}}, \qquad (1.1)$$

where T is the absolute temperature and A is the atomic weight of the gas. In this formula the velocity is given in centimeters per second. It follows from (1.1) that, for example, when $T = 1000°K$, the mean velocity of hydrogen atoms is about 4×10^5 cm per sec, while the mean velocity of mercury atoms is only 3×10^4 cm per sec.

By increasing the temperature from the lowest value (a fraction of a degree above absolute zero, which is possible to achieve by modern methods) to a few thousand degrees[1], it is possible to take practically any material through the three possible states, namely, solid, liquid, and gaseous. It is then natural to ask: How will the properties of the material change if the heating is continued still further and the temperature is increased beyond a few thousand degrees Kelvin? At very high temperatures it is difficult to imagine that the vessel containing the material under investigation will remain solid, since most melting points lie below $3000 - 4000°K$. However, this is a *practical* difficulty which can, as we shall see, be overcome. We shall therefore assume that we have a perfect container whose walls have a higher melting point than any temperature which we shall consider. Under these conditions we shall find that at temperatures as low as $3000 - 5000°K$ there are already signs that certain new processes take place which are associated with a change in the state of the atoms themselves, rather than of the gas as a whole.

It is well known that each atom consists of a positively charged nucleus, which carries practically all the mass of the atom, and a number of electrons which surround the nucleus, forming the electron shell of the atom. This shell, and in particular its outer components, which are relatively weakly bound to the nucleus, has a relatively brittle structure. Thus, when an atom collides with a rapidly moving particle, one of the outer electrons may be removed leaving behind a positively charged ion. This ionization is the most characteristic process for this range of temperatures. We thus arrive at the important result that, when the temperature is high enough, the gas is no longer neutral but contains both positive ions and free electrons. The number of ions and electrons in the gas increases very rapidly with increasing temperature T. When the gas is in thermal equilibrium with the surrounding medium (the walls of the perfect container), most of the atoms will become ionized by the time temperatures of the order of $10,000 - 100,000°K$ have been reached, and there will be practically no neutral atoms left.

[1]All temperatures in this book are given in the absolute units (degrees Kelvin).

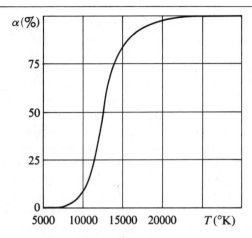

FIGURE 1. *Degree of ionization of hydrogen as a function of temperature.*

The relative number of ionized atoms in hydrogen is shown in Fig. 1 as a function of the temperature. The degree of ionization depends not only on the temperature but also on the density of the gas (though less sensitively). For example, in the case of Fig. 1, the total number of ions and neutral atoms per unit volume was assumed to be 7×10^{16}. At room temperature the pressure corresponding to this density is about 1 mm Hg. It is evident from Fig. 1 that when $T = 10,000°$K, the number of ionized atoms is less than 10% of the total number of hydrogen atoms, while at 30,000°K there is only one neutral atom for every 2×10^4 positive ions (protons).

The electron shell of the hydrogen atom contains only one electron, and therefore the ionization process is completed as soon as this electron is removed. In other atoms the electron shell exhibits a much more complicated structure and the energy which is necessary to remove an electron is very different for the different electrons. The outermost electrons can be fairly easily removed, and, as has already been pointed out, at a temperature of the order of 20,000 – 30,000°K there are practically no neutral atoms left. This means that the gas as a whole is completely ionized. However, this does not mean that the ionization process has been concluded, since there are still a number of electrons left in each of the atoms even after one or more of the outer electrons have been removed. Thus, the larger the atomic number (that is, the number indicating the position of the particular element in the periodic table) the larger the number of electrons in the atom, and the higher the energy necessary to remove the inner electrons. Therefore, the final ionization of heavy atoms, in which even the inner electrons are removed, will occur only at exceedingly high temperatures (of the order of $10^6 - 10^7$ degrees Kelvin). We know that the complete ionization of a heavy gas leads to a situation in which to each positive ion there will be Z free electrons, where Z is the atomic number, that is, the original number of electrons in the neutral atom. However, the gas as a whole remains neutral, since the ionization process as such does not produce an excess of charge of either sign.

At high temperatures the ionization of a gas occurs as a result of the various interactions between the individual atoms on the one hand, and electrons, ions, and radiation, on the other. These interactions are varied and very complicated. We shall, therefore, postpone their description to a later chapter, and for the moment confine our attention to the behavior of the ionized gas as a whole.

A gas in which an appreciable number of atoms or molecules are ionized is referred to as *plasma*. The term plasma was first introduced by the American physicists Langmuir and Tonks in 1923. Plasma is the normal state of matter at temperatures of the order of 10,000°K or more. It is the most common state of matter in nature. For example, the sun and all the stars are nothing else but gigantic condensations of high-temperature plasma. The outer layers of the earth's atmosphere, that is, the ionosphere, are also known to consist of plasma.

In the above discussion we introduced the concept of plasma in terms of the simple process of heating of a gas in a perfect container. In practice, this is neither the best nor the easiest method of producing plasma either in laboratory experiments or in industrial processes. The normal conditions under which plasma is produced are those which prevail in the various forms of gas discharges. When an electric discharge is produced in a gas, a current flows; the current carriers are the electrons and ions which are produced as a result of the ionization of the gas. The ionization process itself is an integral part of the current flow and cannot be separated from it. While the current is flowing, new ions and electrons are being produced all the time, and the degree of ionization is maintained at a definite level. The lightning discharge, the spark, the glow of a neon tube in an advertisement — these are all examples of phenomena which occur in highly ionized plasma. However, there is one important difference between the plasma obtained by heating a gas in a container, and that in the gas discharge. The plasma in the gas discharge is not in thermal equilibrium, but is heated from the outside, since it receives the energy which is released during the passage of the current. Heat is *extracted* from it, either by direct contact with the cold walls of the discharge tube or by heat transfer to a surrounding ordinary gas. The plasma which is produced in a high-intensity gas discharge may have a much higher temperature than the metal, glass, or ordinary gas surrounding it. Moreover, plasma of this kind exhibits a further nonequilibrium property: It consists of a number of components which are not equally heated. These components are electrons, positive ions, and neutral atoms. They are thoroughly mixed just as, for example, the oxygen and hydrogen are in the atmosphere. However, in contrast to an ordinary gas mixture in which all the particles have the same mean kinetic energy of thermal motion, the electrons, ions, and neutral atoms in the plasma of a gas discharge have different mean kinetic energies. As a rule, the electrons have a much higher energy than the ions, and the kinetic energy of the ions may be greater than the energy of the neutral atoms and molecules. It may therefore be said that plasma consists of a mixture of components at different temperatures. It is well known that the average kinetic energy W_T which is associated with the random thermal motion of atoms and molecules is related to the temperature T by the following simple expression:

$$W_T = \frac{3}{2}kT, \tag{1.2}$$

where k is the Boltzmann constant, which is equal to 1.38×10^{-16} erg per deg. We recall that k is equal to the ratio of the universal gas constant R to Avogadro's number, that is, the number of atoms in a gram-atom.

Because the mean kinetic energies of the electrons, ions, and neutral particles in the plasma are different, the plasma as a whole must be regarded in a sense as having three different temperatures, that is, the electron temperature T_e, the ion temperature T_i, and the atomic temperature T_0. Usually, $T_e \gg T_i > T_0$, where the sign $\gg$ means "much greater than." The very large difference between T_e and T_i, which is characteristic of most forms of gas discharge, is due to the very great difference between the mass of the electrons and the mass of the ions. The external sources of electrical energy, which are used to produce and maintain the gas discharge, communicate energy directly to the plasma electrons, since it is the light electrons which act as the current carriers. The ions, on the other hand, obtain their energy by colliding with the rapidly moving electrons. Since the mass of the ions is much greater than the electron mass, the kinetic energy lost by an electron to an ion in an electron-ion collision is quite small. This becomes clear if one considers the collision between a light plastic ball and a heavy steel sphere. Simple calculations, based on the conservation of energy and the conservation of linear momentum, show that if a body of mass m_1 collides with another body having a much greater mass m_2, then the fraction of kinetic energy communicated to the heavier body must be less than $4m_1/m_2$. Therefore, since the ratio of the mass of the electron to the mass of an ion is equal to $1/1840A$, where A is the atomic weight of the atoms from which the ions are produced, the maximum energy which can be received by the ion is only about $2 \times 10^{-3}/A$. It follows that an electron must undergo a very large number of collisions with the ions before it will lose most of its energy. Since the processes in which an exchange of energy takes place between the electrons and ions occur in parallel with the processes in which the electrons receive energy from the external sources of current, there is usually a large temperature difference between the electrons and ions in the gas discharge. Thus, for example, in discharge devices such as neon tubes, mercury rectifiers, and so on, the electron temperature

T_e is usually of the order of 10,000°K, while T_i and T_0 are usually less than one or two thousand degrees. In the arc discharge, which is used in electrical welding, the rate of electron-ion collisions is higher, and this tends to reduce the temperature difference between the electrons and the ions. However, T_e is still greater than T_i, the former being of the order of a few tens of thousands of degrees while T_i and T_0 are of the order of 6000°K. Under certain special conditions the ion temperature of a highly ionized plasma may be much greater than the electron temperature. Such conditions prevail, for example, in the high-power short-lived electrical discharges which are used in studies of the controlled thermonuclear reactions.

1.2 Plasma as a Quasi-neutral Medium

We shall now discuss the definition of plasma and its main properties in somewhat greater detail. In general, a plasma, that is, an ionized gas, may consist of a number of components. Even in the relatively simple case where plasma is produced by ionization of a chemically simple gas, for example, nitrogen, oxygen, or mercury vapor, the ion component will consist of a number of different ions, that is, ions with one, two, three, or more elementary charges. Moreover, in addition to the atomic ions, the plasma may contain molecular ions, and also neutral atoms and molecules. Each of these components can be characterized by a corresponding concentration n and temperature T. In the simplest case, when all the ions are singly charged atomic ions, and the neutral component is fully dissociated and consists of atoms only, the plasma will contain only three components, namely, electrons, ions, and neutral atoms. These conditions will occur only in high-intensity discharges in hydrogen, deuterium, or tritium. In this particular case, the ion concentration n_i is equal to the electron concentration n_e. In the more general case, when the plasma consists of singly charged ions with concentration n_1, doubly charged ions with concentration n_2, and so on, we have the following approximate equation

$$n_e = n_1 + 2n_2 + 3n_3 + \cdots.$$

This shows that the plasma as a whole is quasi-neutral; that is, there is no appreciable surplus of charge of either sign. We must discuss this particular property of plasma in greater detail since it is particularly important and in the final analysis it forms the foundation upon which the definition of plasma is based.

It is natural to ask: To what extent is an ionized gas quasi-neutral? Whatever the method which is used to produce the ionization, it is quite clear *a priori* that the number of positive and negative charges must be the same. Since the velocity of the electrons and of the ions are very different, the former are more likely to leave the region in which they are produced. Therefore, although the number of charges of either sign is originally the same, nevertheless, it would appear that, because the electrons are faster than the ions, they are lost much more quickly to the walls of the discharge tube, and the ions are left behind. On the other hand, it must be remembered that a net loss of electrons from the ionized gas will immediately give rise to an excess charge of the opposite sign, and this will tend to equalize the current of electrons and ions, and to reduce the difference between the concentrations of particles of opposite signs. The conditions under which this effect will be sufficient to maintain the plasma in the quasi-neutral state may be deduced as follows.

Suppose for the sake of simplicity that the ionized gas contains electrons and singly charged ions only. If the plasma is to be quasi-neutral, n_e must be nearly equal to n_i. The question is: How will a difference between n_e and n_i effect the behavoir of the individual particles? It is clear that this will depend on the magnitude of the electric field which is produced as a result of the difference between the two concentrations. There are two extreme cases which will help us to understand this problem. Thus, if the number of charged particles in a given volume is small, then the electric field produced by them is too small to have any effect on their motion and the individual electrons and ions move quite independently of each other. The plasma need not then be quasi-neutral. The opposite case occurs when the charged-particle concentration in a sufficiently large volume is very high. Here the difference between n_e and n_i gives rise to the appearance of an electric field which may be sufficient to equalize the currents and re-establish the quasi-neutral property of the plasma as a whole. In the final analysis everything depends on the ratio, of the potential energy of an individual ion or electron in the electric field produced as a result of the departure from quasi-neutrality to the mean kinetic energy associated with its thermal motion. If the potential energy W_p, corresponding to an appreciable departure of n_e from n_i, is much greater than kT_e, which is a measure of the energy of thermal motion of an electron, then the plasma will be quasi-neutral to a high degree of accuracy. A more detailed analysis of the relationship between W_p and kT_e shows that the plasma as a whole will be quasi-neutral provided

$$r \gg 5\sqrt{\frac{T_e}{n}}, \tag{1.3}$$

where n is the concentration of charged particles (number of electrons per unit volume) and r is a characteristic linear dimension of the region occupied by the ionized gas, for example, the radius of a spherical container. It is quite easy to see why the parameter r should appear in this expression. Thus, at a given charged-particle concentration, the potential due to these particles, and therefore the potential energy of an individual particle, will depend on the size of the region occupied by the particles. The characteristic linear dimensions of the region must therefore necessarily enter into the condition describing the quasi-neutral property of plasma. The quantity $5\sqrt{T_e/n}$ is called the Debye radius after the German physicist who first introduced this quantity in his theory of electrolysis, where the situation is analogous to that in an ionized gas. Henceforth, the Debye radius will be denoted by r_D.

It follows from the condition given by (1.3) that, if the linear dimensions of the region occupied by an ionized gas of given electron concentration n_e and electron temperature T_e is much greater than the Debye radius r_D, then inside this region $n_e \approx n_i$, where the sign $\approx$ means "approximately equal to." Under these conditions, a considerable departure of n_e from n_i will give rise to the appearance of an electric field which will eject particles of one sign (the surplus particles) and will prevent the escape of particles of the other sign. This mechanism automatically maintains the equality of n_e and n_i, and will cease to be effective only when $r \ll r_D$. When the linear dimensions of the region occupied by the gas are much smaller than r_D, the electric fields produced as a result of the difference between n_e and n_i are too small to have any appreciable effect on the motion of the individual particles.

We are now in a position to give a more precise definition of plasma. As long as the relative number of charged particles giving rise to a field is too small to affect their individual motions, there is no point in introducing a new state of matter. The new form of matter which we have called plasma corresponds to the state in which the number of electrons and ions is so large that even a small displacement of the electron component relative to the ion component is impossible, because such a displacement gives rise to strong electric fields tending to prevent any departure from the equality of n_e and n_i. Therefore, an ionized gas can be referred to as plasma if, and only if, the condition given by (1.3) is easily satisfied.

It must be emphasized that the quasi-neutral property of plasma is only observed provided the volume occupied by the plasma is large enough. If we consider a cube with sides of length x inside the plasma, where x is much smaller than r_D, then inside this cube the number of ions may in fact be very different from the number of electrons. However, as the ratio x/r_D increases, the ratio n_e/n_i tends to unity.

1.3 General Nature of the Motion of Charged Particles in Plasma

Although plasma may be regarded as a special form of a gaseous mixture (in the simplest case, a mixture of two components, namely, electron and ion gases), there are many important physical properties in which it differs from an ordinary gas containing only neutral particles. These differences are especially evident in the behavior of plasma in electric and magnetic fields. In distinction to an ordinary neutral gas, which is practically unaffected by electric and magnetic fields, the properties of plasma may be altered very considerably by such fields. An electric field — even a very weak one — gives rise to an electric current in the plasma. In a magnetic field, plasma behaves as a diamagnetic material. It also exhibits a very strong interaction with electromagnetic waves, which is shown, for example, by the fact that radio waves are reflected by plasma as if it were a mirror. This book will be largely concerned with the specific properties, which are exhibited by plasma in its interaction with electric and magnetic fields and serve as the basis for many scientific and technological applications of plasma. In order to understand the nature of these processes, we must first consider the behavior of the individual electrons and ions which make up the plasma. The analysis of the motion of these particles must be based on the following:

1. The laws of motion of electrons and ions in electric and magnetic fields produced by external sources.

2. The elementary interactions between the particles during collisions. The change in the direction of motion of the colliding particles, which occurs during such interactions, may also be accompanied by the production of new charged particles and the appearance of various forms of radiation which then escape from the plasma.

The behavior of the individual particles can be used to interpret the macroscopic properties of plasma as a whole.

Let us now try to describe, in very general terms, the motion of a charged particle in plasma. The path of each electron or ion can at first be regarded very approximately as consisting of segments over which the particle executes free motion without interacting with its neighbors. The free motion of the particle is interrupted by collisions which result in changes in its direction of motion. In the intervals between successive collisions, the particle moves under the action of the general electric or magnetic field produced in the plasma by the external sources. This is a very simplified description of the motion of a plasma particle. It must be augmented by taking into consideration the intrinsic electric field which exists in plasma even in the absence of external sources. Thus, each charged particle produces a radial electric field in its neighborhood. Since the number of particles of both signs is the same, the average internal field must be zero. However, this does

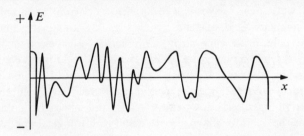

FIGURE 2. *Spatial variation of the internal electric field along a given
direction in plasma at a given instant of time.*

not mean that at every instant of time the electric field at every
point in space is exactly zero. In fact, the field at an internal point
in the plasma exhibits very rapid fluctuations, both in its magnitude
and in its direction. These random fluctuations yield zero average
field, provided that the interval of time over which the average is
taken is long enough.

However, if the electric field is measured at different points in
the plasma at a given instant of time, the resulting distribution is
found to be approximately of the form shown in Fig. 2. The
random space and time variations in the internal field of the
plasma are superimposed on the macroscopic fields due to external
sources. Therefore, the motion of an electron or an ion in plasma
can never be regarded as strictly consisting of free-motion intervals
during which the particle moves under the influence of the average
(that is, the external) field only. The random internal field cannot
be ignored altogether; it is implicit even in our simplified model.
When we say that the effect of all other charged particles in the
plasma on the trajectory of the chosen ion or electron is exhibited
by the collisions between them, we are, in fact, replacing the true
effect, which is due to the interaction of the particle with the
internal microfield, by the device of a collision.

After these preliminary remarks, we can proceed to an analysis
of the free motion of individual charged particles in given electric
and magnetic fields.

Motion of Charged Particles in Electric and Magnetic Fields

2.1 General Laws of Motion for Charged Particles in Electric Fields

The laws governing the motion of a charged particle in an electric field resemble the laws of motion in a gravitational field. Consider Fig. 3 which depicts the trajectories of charged particles in an electric field parallel to the y axis. The arrows indicate the initial velocities of the particles at particular instants of time. The force acting on a charged particle is equal to qE, where q is the charge and E the electric field strength. For singly-charged particles, $q = \pm e$, where e is the elementary electric charge;[2] for multiply-charged ions, q is an integral multiple of e. Under the action of this force, a singly-charged positive ion of mass m_i will undergo an acceleration equal to eE/m_i in the direction of the positive y axis (Fig. 3). The acceleration of an electron would be in the direction of the negative y axis and equal to eE/m_e, where m_e is the mass of the electron. Since an electron is much lighter than an ion, it undergoes a much greater acceleration.

The trajectory of a charged particle in a uniform electric field, that is, a field of constant magnitude and direction, is always a parabola. The specific form of this parabola depends on the properties of the particle, on the initial conditions and on the magnitude of the electric field E. Suppose, for example, that the

---

[2]The elementary charge e is equal to 4.8×10^{-10} esu $= 1.6 \times 10^{-19}$ coulomb.

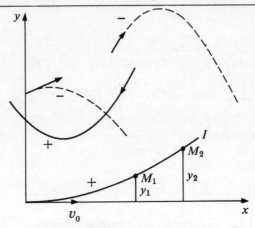

FIGURE 3. *Trajectories of charged particles in a uniform electric field.*

electric field is parallel to the y axis, and that the initial velocity of the particle v_0 is parallel to the x axis (path I in Fig. 3). The motion of the particle in the direction of the x axis is then uniform, whilst in the direction of the y axis it is uniformly accelerated. The coordinates of the particle are given by the formulas

$$x = v_0 t, \qquad y = \frac{qE}{2m}t^2, \qquad (2.1)$$

which are well known from elementary mechanics and represent uniform motion and uniformly-accelerated motion respectively. The time t can be eliminated between these two equations, to give a relation between y and x, that is, to give the equation of the trajectory of the particle. This equation is

$$y = \frac{qE}{2mv_0^2}x^2. \qquad (2.2)$$

It is well known that this represents a parabola. The increase in the velocity of a charged particle, which it assumes in a time t in the direction of the force acting upon it, is $(qE/m)t$. The kinetic energy of the particle, which is equal to $(1/2)mv^2$, does not remain constant during the motion because the electric field does work on the particle. This work is equal to the product of the force acting on the particle and the distance traversed by it in the direction of the field; that is, it is given by $W = qE(y_2 - y_1)$ (see Fig. 3). Therefore

$$\frac{mv_2^2}{2} - \frac{mv_1^2}{2} = qE(y_2 - y_1), \qquad (2.3)$$

where v_1 and v_2 are the velocity of the particle at any two points M_1 and M_2 on the trajectory. We note that the quantity $E(y_2 - y_1)$ is the potential difference between the points M_1 and M_2. Therefore, the right-hand side of Equation (2.3) is the product of the charge of the particle and the potential difference between the end points of the trajectory traversed by the particle. For example, if the particle begins its motion from a state of rest, its kinetic energy at any point on its trajectory will be equal to qU, where U is the potential difference, in electrostatic units, between the initial and final points of the trajectory. If the potential at the initial point is conventionally taken to be equal to zero, then at any other point on the trajectory U will be equal to minus the value of the potential.[3] If U is expressed in practical units, that is, volts (V), then the relation between the kinetic energy and the potential difference traversed by the particle can be written in the following form:

$$\frac{mv^2}{2} = Ze\frac{U}{300} = ZU \cdot 1.6 \cdot 10^{-12}, \qquad (2.4)$$

where $Z = q/e$ is the number of elementary electric charges carried by the particle. The unit of kinetic energy in Equations (2.3) and (2.4) is the erg.

It follows from (2.4) that a singly-charged particle which has traversed the potential difference of 1 volt receives an energy equal to 1.6×10^{-12} erg. However, it is more convenient to express the energy of particles such as electrons and ions directly in terms of the potential difference traversed by them. In this system of units, a convenient unit of energy is the energy attained

[3]A positively-charged particle can only be accelerated along a falling potential. Therefore, if the initial potential is equal to zero, the potential at any other point on the trajectory must be negative.

by a singly-charged particle, for example an electron, on passing through a potential difference of 1 V. This new unit of energy is widely used in electron, atomic, nuclear, and plasma physics, and is referred to as the *electron-volt* (eV). In view of the above definition, 1 eV = 1.6×10^{-12} erg. A particle of charge $q = Ze$ reaches an energy equal to ZU eV on falling through a potential difference U.

We note that an electron with the energy of 1 eV has a velocity of 5×10^7 cm per sec, while a hydrogen ion (proton) of the same energy has a velocity of 1.4×10^6 cm per sec. This velocity is greater than the mean velocity of ordinary hydrogen molecules at room temperature by a factor of approximately 10. The energies of atoms and molecules in neutral gases can also be expressed in terms of electron-volts. All that is required is to divide the kinetic energy, given in ergs, by the conversion factor 1.6×10^{-12}. When this is done, it is found that the molecules or atoms of a gas at room temperature have a mean kinetic energy of about 0.04 eV. The mean kinetic energy of a gas particle reaches 1 eV at about 7600°K. In stellar interiors, where the temperatures are believed to be of the order of ten million degrees, the mean energy of the constituent particles is of the order of some thousands of electron-volts.

2.2   The Motion of a Particle in the Field of a Point Charge

So far, we have only considered the simple case of a charged particle in a (uniform) electric field whose intensity is the same at all points of space. In a more complicated field, the trajectory of the particle will no longer be a parabola. However, Equation (2.4), which gives the relation between the change in the kinetic energy and the potential difference traversed by the particle, is still valid in this general case. The increase (or decrease) in the kinetic energy between two points in space is always given by the potential difference between the two points and — this must be especially emphasized — is independent of the particular path traversed by the particle between the two points. Among the many special cases of the motion of electrons and ions in an electric field, a particularly interesting one is the motion in a radial field, that is, the field produced by a point charge. This case corresponds to the interaction between the individual electrons and ions in plasma. Figure 4 illustrates a *coulomb collision* between an electron and a plasma ion in which the two colliding particles interact through their electric fields. The precise form of the trajectory of a charged particle in the field of a point charge can only be determined by mathematical methods which are outside the scope of the present book. However, the most important property of the trajectory, that is, the magnitude of the angle ϑ through which the particle is deflected as a result of the interaction with the center of force, may be approximately estimated in a very simple way. Suppose that the center of force is located at the point 0 (Fig. 4) and that the incident particle passes it at a large distance, so that the deflection from its original direction of motion is small. The minimum distance between the incident particle and the charge at the point 0 will then be approximately the same as the *impact parameter b*, which is equal to the length of the perpendicular dropped from the point 0 on to the extension of the original direction of motion of the particle (the line *AB* in Fig. 4). Since the force acting on the particle is inversely proportional to the square of the distance from the center of force 0, it follows that most of the interaction between the incident particle and the center of force takes place over a small part of its trajectory, in the immediate neighborhood of the point of closest approach to 0. Suppose that this part of the trajectory occupies the region A_1A_2 in Fig. 4. For very approximate calculations it may be assumed that the length of this part of the trajectory is equal to

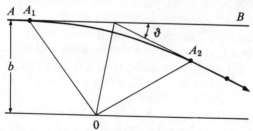

FIGURE 4. *Trajectory of a charged particle in the field of a point charge of opposite sign.*

twice the impact parameter (at the ends of this segment, the force acting on the particle is reduced by one-half as compared with its value at the point of closest approach). A particle having a velocity v will traverse the segment A_1A_2 in a time equal to $2b/v$. During this time, the force acting upon it will be approximately perpendicular to its path. This force may be approximated to be equal to q_1q_2/b^2, where q_1 and q_2 are the two interacting charges. As a matter of fact, the mean force will be smaller, but the true time of interaction will be greater than that assumed here. During the time taken by the particle to traverse the segment A_1A_2, this force will transmit to the particle a velocity equal to

$$\frac{1}{m} \cdot \frac{q_1q_2}{b^2} \cdot \frac{2b}{v}$$

in the direction perpendicular to the initial direction of motion, where m is the mass of the particle. The ratio of this velocity to the initial velocity v must be equal to the tangent of the angle of deflection ϑ (see Fig. 4), and since in the case of small deflections $\tan \vartheta$ is approximately equal to ϑ, we have

$$\vartheta \sim \frac{2q_1q_2}{mv^2b}, \tag{2.5}$$

where the symbol $\sim$ indicates that the expression is only very roughly true; that is, it gives the order of magnitude of ϑ and the true result may be different by an appreciable factor. Such approximate expressions are widely used in modern physics and are frequently just as useful as the precise formulas. Approximate calculations are useful whenever we have to analyze complicated phenomena involving a large number of different factors. Under such conditions, it is first necessary to ascertain the relative importance of the various factors. A typical example is the expression for the Debye radius given by (1.3). There is very little point in trying to establish the exact value of this quantity since the concept of the Debye radius is introduced in order to distinguish between two extreme cases in the behavior of a system of charged particles, namely, (1) when the particles are independent of each other, and (2) when they form a plasma.

Approximate formulas are a very powerful tool in the elucidation of the general physical properties of a phenomenon because they are free from the detail which has to be introduced in a more rigorous mathematical calculation. Equation (2.5) is valid — in the sense indicated above — only for those values of b which correspond to a deflection much smaller than 1 radian. The precise relation between ϑ and b, which is valid for all values of the impact parameter, may be derived by means of a rigorous theoretical analysis of the motion of a charged particle in the field of a point charge. The exact result is

$$\tan\frac{\vartheta}{2} = \frac{q_1 q_2}{mv^2 b}. \tag{2.6}$$

For large b, that is, when the particles pass each other at a large distance, this formula is identical with (2.5), and this justifies the very approximate estimate previously derived. The range of applicability of the formula may be illustrated by the following special case: The deflection experienced by a 1 eV electron when it interacts with a singly-charged ion at an impact parameter $b = 10^{-6}$ cm is about 0.14 rad, that is, about 8.5°. The magnitude of the deflection decreases with increasing energy.

2.3 Optical Analogy for the Motion of a Charged Particle in an Electric Field

The above two examples, namely, motion in a uniform and in a radial electric field exhaust all the possibilities as far as the problems encountered in plasma physics are concerned. However, it will be useful to consider one further special case which is interesting because it will be found to exhibit certain very important general properties.

Consider a charged particle (in order to be specific, suppose that it is an electron) passing through the boundary separating two regions of space at different potentials (Fig. 5). This means that, in a very thin boundary layer between the two regions, there is a very strong electric field giving rise to a sudden drop in the potential For the sake of simplicity, we shall suppose that the boundary

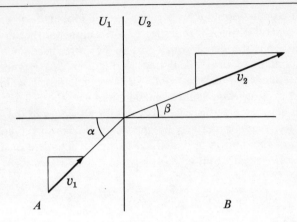

FIGURE 5. *Trajectory of a particle passing through the boundary between two regions at different potentials.*

layer is infinitely. In thin practice, this can never be realized exactly but it is possible to approach this situation approximately under certain special conditions. If the potential is measured relative to the point at which the velocity of the electron was zero, Equation (2.4) will remain valid over the entire trajectory of the electron. Suppose that at the boundary the potential changes from U_1 to U_2. Since the potentials on either side of the boundary are constant, an electron will experience no forces, either before or after passing through the boundary layer. It will therefore execute straight-line motion both in region A and in region B. However, in the very short interval of time during which it is within the boundary layer, it experiences a very strong force at right-angles to the boundary of separation between A and B. This force either increases or decreases the component of the velocity of the electron perpendicular to the boundary. The component which is parallel to the boundary remains unaltered. This means that the trajectory must show a discontinuity at the boundary, as shown in Fig. 5. The case illustrated in this figure corresponds to an *acceleration* of the electron in the boundary layer. Suppose that v_1 and v_2 are the velocities of the electron in the two regions A and B respectively, and let the angles between these velocities and the normal to the boundary be denoted by α and β. Since the velocity component parallel to the surface remains unaltered, it follows that

$$v_1 \sin\alpha = v_2 \sin\beta.$$

When $Z = 1$, it follows from Equation (2.4) that $\frac{1}{2}mv_1^2 = eU_1$, $\frac{1}{2}mv_2^2 = eU_2$. When these equations are combined, it is found that

$$\frac{\sin\alpha}{\sin\beta} = \frac{v_2}{v_1} = \sqrt{\frac{U_2}{U_1}}. \qquad (2.7)$$

The mathematical form of this result shows a striking similarity to the law of refraction of light rays. It is well known that when a light ray passes from a medium A to a medium B, its direction of propagation changes in accordance with the relation

$$\frac{\sin\alpha}{\sin\beta} = \frac{n_2}{n_1}, \qquad (2.7a)$$

where α and β are the angles of incidence and refraction, and n_1 and n_2 are the refractive indices of the two media. Comparison of Equations (2.7) and (2.7a) will show that an electron beam passing through the boundary between two regions at different potentials behaves in a way which is analogous to the behavior of light rays in optics. In the present context, the square root of the potential plays the role of the refractive index. It may be shown that the analogy between the mechanics of charged particles in an electrostatic field and the laws governing the propagation of light rays is very much wider than would be supposed on the basis of the above example. In point of fact, any electric field may be imagined as consisting of a very large number of thin layers, each of which corresponds to an approximately constant potential which changes discontinuously by a small amount on passing from one layer to the next (Fig. 6). In such a field, the trajectory of a particle will consist of a large number of very short, straight segments with breaks, at the points of transition from one layer to another, at which the trajectories are refracted in accordance with (2.7). The optical analogue of this situation is the propagation of a light ray through a transparent medium with a varying refractive index. Therefore, the motion of charged particles in electrostatic fields is fully analo-

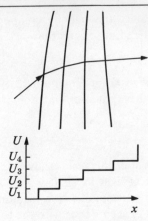

FIGURE 6. *Motion of a particle in an electric field of a slowly varying potential. U_1, U_2, U_3, ... represent the potentials of the regions into which the space may be subdivided.*

gous to the propagation of light rays. This fact is used in the design of electronic instruments which are analogous to optical apparatus, for example, the electron-optical converter, the electrostatic electron microscope, and so on. Analysis of the general similarity between ordinary mechanics and geometrical optics has led to the development of modern quantum mechanics, which provides a very satisfactory description of all atomic phenomena. However, all this is outside the scope of the present book, which is exclusively concerned with the physics of plasma.

2.4 Motion in an Alternating Electric Field

All of our previous discussion was concerned with time-independent electric fields. However, in order to understand certain phenomena which take place in plasma, it will be useful to consider the behavior of electrons and ions in rapidly varying electric fields. All the main features of the interaction of an alternating field with a charged particle can be explained by analyzing the following simple example: Suppose that the electric field-strength is a periodic function of time at all points in space. The dependence of E on time is then

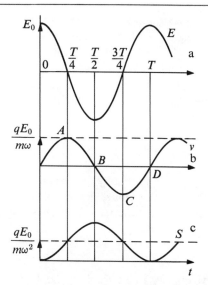

FIGURE 7. *Motion of a charged particle in an alternating electric field:*
a. *variation in the field strength,* b. *variation in the velocity of the particle,*
c. *displacement of the particle in the direction of the field.*

of the form shown in Fig. 7a (a cosine curve). The distance between
successive crests of the curve is defined as the period T of the oscillations, while the frequency ν, that is, the number of oscillations per
second, is related to T by the obvious formula $\nu = 1/T$. A quantity
often used in physics is the *angular frequency*, which is usually
denoted by ω and is equal to $2\pi\nu$, so that $\omega = 2\pi/T$. The equation
of the cosine curve shown in Fig. 7a may then be written in the
following form:

$$E = E_0 \cos 2\pi t/T = E_0 \cos \omega t.$$

The field strength reaches its maximum value at times $t = 0,\ T$,
$2T, \ldots$ and is equal to zero at $t = T/4,\ 3T/4,\ 5T/4, \ldots$, and so on.
Suppose now that a charged particle with zero velocity is placed in
the electric field at time $t = 0$. The particle will immediately be accelerated in the direction of the field (if its charge is positive) so
that its velocity will increase during the first quarter of the period

and will reach its maximum value when the field is zero (point A in Fig. 7b). The magnitude of the maximum velocity is proportional to the force acting on the particle during the acceleration, and inversely proportional to the mass of the particle. If the field strength were constant during the first quarter of the period and equal to its maximum value, the velocity of the particle at time $t = T/4$ would be

$$\frac{qE_0}{m}\cdot\frac{T}{4} = \frac{\pi}{2}\cdot\frac{qE_0}{m\omega}.$$

Since, however, the field gradually decreases, the final velocity will, in fact, be smaller than this value. Exact calculations show that the velocity of the particle at time $t = T/4$ is given by

$$v_{\max} = \frac{qE_0}{m\omega}. \qquad (2.8)$$

During the next quarter of the period, the field changes sign, the particle is decelerated, and its velocity becomes zero at the end of the second quarter-period (point B in Fig. 7b). As soon as this point is passed the particle, accelerated in the opposite direction, reaches a maximum negative value equal to $-v_{\max}$ at time $t = 3T/4$, and then again returns to zero at the point D, that is, after one complete period of the electric field. The whole process is then repeated periodically. The graph showing the variation in the velocity of the particle is shifted relative to the graph of the field E by one-quarter of the period. When E is at a maximum, the velocity is zero, while zero values of the field correspond to maximum velocities ($\pm v_{\max}$).

Consider now the variation in the length of the path traversed by the particle. In the time interval between 0 and $T/4$, the particle begins to move in the direction of the field and eventually acquires its maximum velocity. The motion in this direction continues throughout this time interval, as long as the velocity is positive. The displacement reaches the maximum positive value at time $t = T/2$, which corresponds to the maximum negative value of E. During the next half-period, the particle moves in the opposite direction and eventually returns to the original position at the end of the period. The process is then repeated periodically. A plot of the position of the particle as a function of time is shown in Fig. 7c. This curve is exactly out of phase with that showing the variation in the field E with time, that is, the minima of one correspond to the maxima of the other.

The equation of the curve representing the position of the particle as a function of time can be written in the following form:

$$S = \frac{qE_0}{m\omega^2}(1 - \cos \omega t). \tag{2.9}$$

In practice, the electric field cannot be established instantaneously but its amplitude gradually increases until it reaches the value E_0 after a number of complete periods. This is illustrated in Fig. 8, in which the electric field is plotted as a function of time t. Calculations show that in this most important case, after the amplitude E_0 has been reached, the oscillations of the particle in space can be described by

$$S = -\frac{qE_0}{m\omega^2} \cos \omega t, \tag{2.10}$$

which differs from the preceding expression by a constant term which is independent of time. In the present case, the curve representing the displacement S will be the mirror image of the curve representing the electric field E. This concludes our brief description of the motion of a charged particle in an alternating electric field. The results we have obtained will be used later when

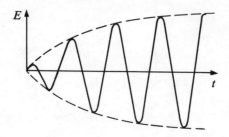

FIGURE 8. *Growth of the amplitude of an alternating electric field.*

we come to analyze the interaction of plasma with electromagnetic waves.

2.5   The Motion of Charged Particles in a Uniform Magnetic Field

Consider now the motion of electrons and ions in a magnetic field. The force F which acts on a particle of charge q and velocity v in a magnetic field H is equal to $(qvH/c)\sin\theta$, where θ is the angle between the directions of v and H and c is the velocity of light ($c = 3 \times 10^{10}$ cm per sec). This force is perpendicular to both v and H and the three variables v, H, and F form a right-handed system. This means that the directions of v, H, and F are given respectively by the thumb, index finger, and the middle finger of the right hand, when the three fingers are at right-angles to each other. In the case of negative q, the force acts in the opposite direction. In the abbreviated language of vector analysis, this is represented by the simple formula

$$F = \frac{q}{c}\mathbf{v} \times \mathbf{H}, \tag{2.11}$$

where the symbol $\mathbf{v} \times \mathbf{H}$ is called the *vector product*. By definition, the magnitude of the vector product of two vectors $\mathbf{A}$ and $\mathbf{B}$ is equal to $\mathbf{AB}\sin\theta$, where θ is the angle between them, while its direction forms a right-handed system with $\mathbf{A}$ and $\mathbf{B}$ (Fig. 9). All this leads to the following two consequences:

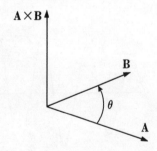

FIGURE 9. *Vector product of two vectors* $\mathbf{A}$ *and* $\mathbf{B}$.

1. If a charged particle moves in the direction of the magnetic field, then $F = 0$, since $\theta = 0$. If, on the other hand, the particle moves at right-angles to the direction of the field, then $F = qvH/c$.

2. The force F is always perpendicular to the velocity of the particle. It therefore does no work and can have no effect on the *magnitude* of the velocity of the particle.

The simplest case is that of the motion of a charged particle in a uniform magnetic field, that is, a field which can be represented by parallel lines of force whose magnitude H is the same at all points of the space occupied by the field. A field of this kind can be produced, for example, between the plane pole pieces of a large electromagnet or inside a uniformly wound solenoid. Suppose now that the velocity of a charged particle is perpendicular to the magnetic field. The force acting on the particle is then constant at all points along its path and is equal to qvH/c. Since the force is perpendicular to the velocity, it gives rise to a centripetal acceleration with the result that the direction of the velocity undergoes a continuous variation. In this particular case, the acceleration is also constant in magnitude (because v and H are constant). Therefore, the particle moves in a plane perpendicular to the direction of H on a curvilinear trajectory with constant centripetal acceleration (Fig. 10). It is known from elementary mechanics that under these conditions the trajectory must take the form of a circle. According to the second law of Newton, the force which maintains a particle on a circular trajectory is equal to the product of its mass and the

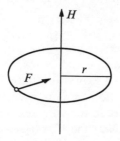

FIGURE 10. *Motion of a charged particle in a transverse magnetic field, that is, in the case when $v \perp H$.*

centripetal acceleration, v^2/r, where r is the radius of the circle. Therefore

$$\frac{mv^2}{r} = \frac{1}{c}qvH,$$

and hence

$$r = \frac{mvc}{qH}. \tag{2.12}$$

The quantity r is called the Larmor radius after the British physicist Larmor, who investigated the laws of motion of charged particles in a magnetic field at the end of the nineteenth century. In practice, the most convenient form of this expression is that in which the radius r is expressed in terms of the energy of the particle. This formula can be obtained from (2.12) and is found to be

$$r = 1.12 \cdot 10^{14} \frac{\sqrt{mW}}{ZH}, \tag{2.13}$$

where Z is the number of elementary charges carried by the particle and W is its energy in electron-volts. For an electron, $m = 9 \times 10^{-28}$ g and $Z = 1$. Therefore, the Larmor radius of an electron is given by

$$r_e = \frac{3.4\sqrt{W}}{H}. \tag{2.14}$$

The radius of curvature of the trajectory of a proton for the same values of H and W is greater by a factor of 42, that is,

$$r_p = \frac{143\sqrt{W}}{H}. \tag{2.15}$$

In order to find the Larmor radius for a singly-charged ion of atomic weight A, this last expression must be multiplied by $\sqrt{A}$. Equations (2.14) and (2.15) are illustrated in Figs. 11a and 11b. The various straight lines in these figures correspond to magnetic field-strengths of 100, 1,000, and 10,000 Oersteds. In order to cover as large a range of energies as possible, W and r are plotted on logarithmic scales.

Equation (2.12) can easily be used to determine two other

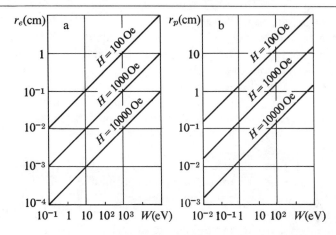

FIGURE 11. *Dependence of the Larmor radius on the energy:*
a. *electrons*, b. *protons*.

quantities characterizing the motion of a particle, namely, the period T_H and the angular velocity ω_H. It is clear that

$$vT_H = 2\pi r, \tag{2.16}$$

and therefore substituting for r from equation (2.12), we have

$$T_H = \frac{2\pi mc}{qH}. \tag{2.17}$$

The angular velocity is related to T_H by

$$\omega_H = \frac{2\pi}{T_H},$$

and therefore

$$\omega_H = \frac{qH}{mc}. \tag{2.18}$$

The quantity ω_H is also called the *angular frequency* or the *Larmor frequency* of the particle.

It follows from (2.17) and (2.18) that the rotational period and the Larmor frequency are independent of the velocity of the particle, since v does not enter into the expressions for T_H and ω_H. The Larmor frequency of electrons is very high and therefore the period is very small, even in very weak magnetic fields. For example, when $H = 1$ Oe, the Larmor frequency is equal to 1.8×10^{-7} cps, which is in the radio frequency range. The directions of motion of electrons and ions in a magnetic field are opposite. A positive ion rotates in a clockwise direction if its path is viewed against the magnetic field. An electron moves in the opposite direction and its trajectory forms a right-handed system with the magnetic field. (The trajectory can be generated by clockwise rotation about the positive direction of the magnetic field.)

We note that a charged particle moving on a circle gives rise to an electric current. The direction of the current due to the motion of electrons and ions in a given magnetic field is the same because particles of different signs move in opposite directions. Each elementary current ring associated with the circular motion of a charged particle is itself a source of a magnetic field (Fig. 12). It is quite easy to show that the field due to a Larmor ring current is always opposite to the direction of the external field producing the circular motion. The circulating particle behaves as if it were trying to reduce the field forcing it into the circular path. The magnitude of the magnetic field due to the circular motion of an electron or ion is very small. However, if the density of the charged particles is high enough, the resultant magnetic field may appreciably reduce the external field in the region occupied by the particles. This effect will be discussed in detail later.

Consider now a more general case of the motion of a charged

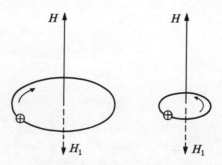

FIGURE 12. *Magnetic field H_1 produced by a charged particle during its motion in an external magnetic field H.*

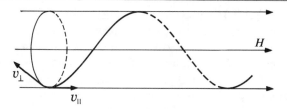

FIGURE 13. *Motion of a charged particle in a uniform magnetic field.*

particle in a uniform magnetic field; that is, suppose that the velocity of the particle v makes an angle α with the direction of the lines of force, where α is less than 90°. The velocity can be resolved into two components which are respectively parallel and perpendicular to the magnetic field, namely, $v_{||} = v \cos \alpha$ and $v_{\perp} = v \sin \alpha$. The magnetic field will only affect the perpendicular component and will force the particle into a circular motion in the plane perpendicular to the vector **H**. The radius of the resulting circle is given, as before, by

$$r = \frac{mv_{\perp}c}{qH} = \frac{mvc}{qH} \sin \alpha.$$

At the same time, the particle will move with a constant velocity $v_{||}$ in the direction of the lines of force. The resultant motion is therefore made up of a uniform rotation and a uniform translation, and can be represented by a screw thread (Fig. 13.) The pitch of the screw, that is, the distance traversed by the particle in the direction of the field during a complete rotation about the lines of force, is given by

$$v_{||}T = \frac{2\pi mvc}{qH} \cos \alpha. \tag{2.19}$$

For small angles α the trajectory is very shallow. For values of α approaching 90° it resembles a compressed spring.

2.6 General Nature of the Motion of Charged Particles in a Nonuniform Magnetic Field

Both in nature and in the apparatus employed for scientific and technological purposes, the motion of charged particles usually takes place in nonuniform magnetic fields. In such fields the direction of the vector **H** varies in space from point to point. A non-uniform magnetic field may have a very complicated geometric form and therefore the trajectories of the charged particles may also be very complicated and tangled. There is little hope of finding a general law which would apply to all such trajectories. However, the situation is considerably simplified if one considers only those particles for which the Larmor radius is relatively small. This means that the magnitude of *r* is small in comparison with the distance over which the field changes appreciably or, in the language of physics, in comparison with the characteristic linear dimension of the field irregularities. A particle with a small Larmor radius does not easily "see" the field irregularities and must complete a large number of rotations about the lines of force before it passes through a region in which there is an appreciable change in

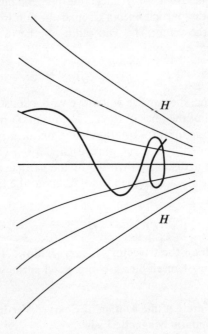

FIGURE 14a. *Trajectory of a charged particle moving in the direction of increasing field strength.*

the field. The effect of field irregularities on the path of a particle of this kind is only important if we consider a sufficiently long segment of its trajectory.

In order to investigate such effects, consider a case where the field strength varies in the direction of the lines of force. This is illustrated in Fig. 14a. The field strength increases from left to right and therefore the lines of force form a converging system (the stronger the field the greater the number of lines per unit area). What will be the behavior of a particle entering a region of this kind? At first sight, it would appear that, provided r is small, the radius of curvature of the trajectory will be inversely proportional to the field H and therefore the pitch of the helical path will decrease, that is, there will be a contraction in all the dimensions by the same factor. However, this implicitly assumes that the angle α between the velocity of the particle and the lines of force is constant. In point of fact, this assumption is not valid because in a nonuniform field the particle experiences a force which is always in the direction of decreasing H. The force retards the particle as it moves from left to right and therefore reduces the longitudinal component $v \cos \alpha$. Since the magnitude of the resultant velocity in a magnetic field remains constant, this can only result in a change in the angle α, which increases, and therefore the transverse component $v \sin \alpha$ also increases. It follows that the ratio of the two velocity components is no longer constant, and the trajectory of a particle entering the increasing field becomes more and more curved, as shown in Fig. 14a.

In order to establish the origin of the retarding force, consider Fig. 14b, which shows a complete turn of the trajectory in an increasing field (it is assumed for the sake of simplicity that the longitudinal component of the velocity is zero). The arrow MA represents the magnetic field at the point M on the trajectory of the particle. This vector can be resolved into two components — one in the direction perpendicular to the plane of the trajectory and the other along the radius of the trajectory. In a uniform magnetic field the lines of force are parallel and the vector **H** has only the single component MB. This component gives rise to the centripetal force F_1, which maintains the circular motion of the particle. The

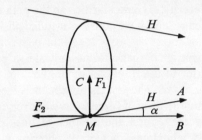

FIGURE 14b. *Forces acting on a charged particle in a magnetic field with converging lines of force. The force F_1 maintains the Larmor circulation, whilst the force F_2 acts in the direction of decreasing field.*

component MC, which is due to the divergence of the lines of force, that is, the nonuniformity of the field, gives rise to a force whose direction is quite easy to find with the aid of the general rule given at the beginning of the present section. This force must be perpendicular to MC and to the velocity, that is, to the arc of the circle at M. This results in the force F_2 which tends to accelerate the particle towards the region of the weaker field.

The same result can also be obtained in a different way. It has been pointed out earlier that the Larmor circle described by a particle in a magnetic field is equivalent to a current and that this current gives rise to a magnetic field which acts in a direction opposite to the external magnetic field in which the particle executes a circular motion. This means that the Larmor circle exhibits properties which enable us to regard it as the analogue of a particle of diamagnetic material, since a diamagnet is defined as a substance in which an external field induces a field of opposite sign. This means that diamagnets are repelled by strong magnetic fields. A "diamagnetic" Larmor circle which is produced by a circulating charged particle will therefore also experience a force tending to accelerate it into the region of weaker field.

It has already been noted that, since the total velocity of a particle in a magnetic field is constant, the deceleration, during the motion along a line of force in the direction of a stronger field, must necessarily be accompanied by an increase in the transverse velocity component. Therefore, the magnetic field H and the magnitude of the transverse velocity component $v_\perp$ should be related to each other. Detailed calculations show that this is so: The square of the transverse component $v_\perp$ is very nearly proportional to H, and therefore the ratio $v_\perp^2/H$ remains almost constant. Since $v_\perp^2$ is proportional to the kinetic energy of the Larmor rotation $W_\perp$, it follows that the condition $v_\perp^2/H = $ const is equivalent to $W_\perp/H = $ const.

This approximate theoretical result has one very important consequence. The word "approximate" must be understood to mean that the quantity $v_\perp^2/H$ may undergo a large number of small changes about a mean value. These variations lie between relatively narrow limits, within which the quantities $v_\perp^2$ and H themselves may vary very considerably. The degree to which $v_\perp^2/H$ remains constant is greater for small Larmor radii, that is, small v and large H.) This ratio is often called an *adiabatic invariant*, which is taken to represent the approximate constancy (in the above sense) of this quantity. Since the ratio $v_\perp^2/H$ is constant, the angular velocity of the particle is proportional to the square root of the magnetic field, and therefore the Larmor radius $r = mv_\perp c/qH$ in a field of varying strength is proportional to $1/\sqrt{H}$.

Since the magnitude of the resultant velocity v is constant, the quantity $\sin^2\alpha/H$ is also an adiabatic invariant for a given particle. Suppose that at some initial point on the trajectory the magnetic field is H_0, while the angle between the velocity and the direction of the lines of force is α_0. The angle at some other point on the trajectory can be found from the relation $\sin^2\alpha/H = \sin^2\alpha_0/H_0$, and hence

$$\sin\alpha = \sin\alpha_0\sqrt{\frac{H}{H_0}}. \tag{2.20}$$

When the particle moves toward the region of stronger field, the angle α continues to increase until it reaches 90°. This occurs at the point at which the right-hand side of (2.20) is equal to unity. The magnitude of the magnetic field H at this point can be found from

$$1 = \sin\alpha_0\sqrt{\frac{H}{H_0}},$$

which yields

$$H = \frac{H_0}{\sin^2\alpha_0}. \tag{2.21}$$

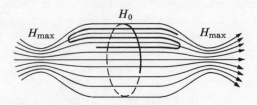

FIGURE 15. *Magnetic mirrors.*

This is the maximum magnetic field which can be reached by a particle with given α_0 since $\sin \alpha$ can never exceed unity. Therefore, having reached the point at which H is given by (2.21), the particle will change its direction of longitudinal motion and will return to the region of lower field. Therefore, high-field regions may, under certain conditions, act as magnetic mirrors. In particular, suppose that the field is of the form shown in Fig. 15. In this field configuration, the magnitude of H increases on either side of the central region and the density of the magnetic lines of force reaches a maximum on the left and on the right of this region. (The maximum and the minimum field strengths are denoted by $H_{\max}$ and H_0, respectively.) Consider the motion of an ion or electron which was originally in the central region. The eventual fate of this particle will depend on the magnitude of α_0. If $\sin \alpha_0 < \sqrt{H_0/H_{\max}}$, the particle will be retarded as it approaches the region of maximum field but will, nevertheless, be able to pass through it. If, on the other hand, $\sin \alpha > \sqrt{H_0/H_{\max}}$, the particle will be reflected by the magnetic mirrors. The particle will be trapped in the space between the two mirrors. This is a simple case of a *magnetic trap* which is capable of retaining charged particles. A trap of this kind can be produced, for example, with the aid of two coils which are parallel to each other and carry electric currents in the same direction.

The intensity of the magnetic field can vary not only along the lines of force but also in the direction at right-angles to them. Thus, for example, the field due to a current flowing in a straight wire decreases with increasing distance from the wire, although the neighboring lines of force are parallel because they are in the form of concentric circles. The trajectory of a charged particle in a non-

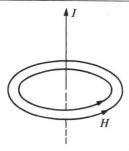

FIGURE 16. *Magnetic field due to a straight-line current.*

uniform field of this kind will, in general, be of a complicated form. However, we can try to understand the situation by considering a number of special cases. If the velocity of a particle is perpendicular to the lines of force, the motion will take the form shown in Fig. 17. (The plane of this figure is parallel to the current of Fig. 16.) The intensity of the magnetic field is assumed to decrease from left to right. The plane trajectory of the particle will then no longer be a circle since the radius of curvature given by (2.12) will be greater on the right than on the left and the particle will describe a spiral. There will therefore be a resultant motion in the direction of the y axis which is parallel to the current of Fig. 16. After a large number of revolutions, the situation will appear as if the particle were moving in an expanding groove whose width depends on the velocity of the particle and the intensity of the magnetic field. The direction of the vertical displacement of the particle depends on its sign. In Fig. 17, the positive ion moves from bottom to top and covers the vertical distance ab in a complete revolution, while an electron moves from top to bottom and the corresponding vertical displacement is cd.

This type of motion is referred to as *magnetic drift* or drift in a nonuniform magnetic field. The word "drift," which is taken from marine terminology, is meant to indicate that the velocity of displacement of the particle along the groove mentioned above is small in comparison with its Larmor velocity. We note that, during the drift, the particle does not escape into a region of stronger or weaker field. On the contrary, during its motion along

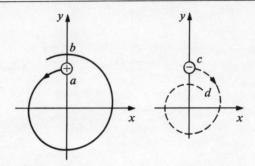

FIGURE 17. *The drift of charged particles moving in a nonuniform magnetic field in the plane perpendicular to H.*

the relatively narrow groove it behaves as if it were tending to retain the same magnetic field within the limits of its trajectory.

Suppose now that the particle moves along a line of force in a nonuniform field whose intensity increases at right angles to the vector **H**. An example of this is shown in Fig. 18, where a positive ion is shown moving in the direction of the field due to a straight-line current. It is clear that the particle cannot continue along the line of force. If its velocity is parallel to the field, the force is zero, and therefore there should be no centripetal acceleration. Hence an ion whose velocity at the point M_1 is parallel to the direction of the field will leave the circular line of force because

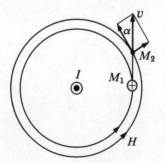

FIGURE 18. *Motion of a positive ion along a magnetic line of force due to a straight-line current.*

of its inertia. During its subsequent motion, the ion will intersect the neighboring lines of force at small angles. For example, at the point M_2 the angle between the velocity of the ion and the field vector **H** may be, say, α. Since the velocity of the ion is now no longer strictly parallel to the lines of force, the particle will experience a force of $\frac{1}{c}qvH \sin\alpha$. In the present case, this force is parallel to the current producing the magnetic field. As a result, the ion is given a velocity component in the direction of the positive y axis and this is, in fact, the drift velocity of the particle in the nonuniform field. The situation is the same in the case of electrons, except that they drift in the opposite direction. It is easy to show that the drift of a particle, due to the presence of a longitudinal component to its velocity, occurs in the same direction as the drift of a particle whose velocity is perpendicular to H.

Calculations show that in the general case, when the particle has both a transverse velocity $v_\perp$ and a longitudinal velocity $v_{||}$, the drift velocity is given by

$$u_d = \frac{1}{\omega_H R}\left(v_{||}^2 + \frac{1}{2}v_\perp^2\right), \tag{2.22}$$

where R is the radius of curvature of the line of force passing through a given point on the trajectory and $\omega_H = qH/mc$ is the Larmor frequency. The direction of the drift velocity u_d is perpendicular both to H and to the radius of curvature of the line of force. In the language of vector analysis, this means that when $q > 0$, the drift-velocity vector $\mathbf{u}_d$ is parallel to the vector product $\mathbf{H} \times \mathbf{R}$.

It follows from the above discussion that the direction of the drift velocity is always such as to oppose any change in H. Equation (2.22) and all the other formulas discussed in this section are strictly valid only when the field is not highly nonuniform, that is, when the change in the magnetic field within the limits of a Larmor circle is small. Under these conditions, $u_d \ll v$; that is, the drift motion contributes a relatively small correction to the velocity of the particle. It should be noted that there is one further condition which limits the range of applicability of Equation (2.22): A particle moving in the space between the conductors giving rise to the magnetic field must not enter the conductors, which is equivalent to saying that the particle must not enter the region in which a current is flowing. When this condition is not satisfied, the equation for the drift velocity becomes more complicated, but all the qualitative effects described above remain. When the drift takes place across the lines of force, both velocity components, $v_{||}$ and $v_\perp$, remain constant in magnitude. In view of the above analysis, the magnitude of H along the drift groove is also constant. It follows that $v_\perp^2/H = $ const and this means that the drift motion does not affect the adiabatic invariance of $v_\perp^2/H$.

In order to obtain a clearer picture of the motion of a charged particle in a slowly varying (in space) magnetic field, we note that this motion may be resolved into two simpler component motions, namely, the Larmor motion with a velocity $v_\perp = v \sin\alpha$ and a displacement of the center of the Larmor circle. The latter, in its turn, can be resolved into motion along the lines of force with the velocity $v_{||} = v \cos\alpha$ and a slow drift at right-angles to the lines of force with the velocity u_d.

The general situation may be illustrated by a number of simple examples. One of these is the motion of a charged particle in the field of a straight conductor carrying a current. The motion of a charged particle in the Earth's magnetic field may be taken as another example. The drift motion in the field of a straight-line current may be described with the aid of Equation (2.22). We shall confine our attention to the case when $\alpha = 90°$ and, therefore, $v_\perp = v$. Under this assumption, Equations (2.22) and (2.12) yield

$$u_d = v\frac{r}{R},$$

where r is the Larmor radius of the trajectory of the particle and R is the radius of curvature of the line of force. In the present case R is equal to the distance from the current. Suppose, for example, that the current is equal to 10^5 amperes and a 100 electron-volt proton is at a distance of 10 cm from the conductor. We thus have $r/R = 7 \times 10^{-2}$ and therefore u_d is quite small in comparison with v, and is equal to 1×10^6 cm per sec. Thus, the particle

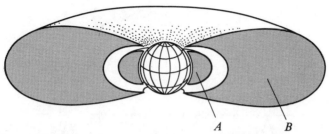

FIGURE 19. *Schematic representation of the earth's radiation belts: A — inner belt, B — outer belt.*

drifts slowly, parallel to the straight current, at a constant distance from it.

The other case is represented in nature by the *radiation belts* surrounding the Earth. The existence of these belts was first established during the flights of the first satellites and space rockets. They consist of electrons and ions of high energy (electron energies up to several million electron-volts, protons, and light nuclei with energies higher by two or three orders of magnitude). These particles are trapped in the Earth's magnetic field. The disposition of the radiation belts in the Earth's neighborhood is illustrated schematically in Fig. 19. As can be seen, two belts can be distinguished, although, in fact, there is no clear dividing boundary between them. The inner belt is at an average distance of a few thousand kilometers from the Earth, even though its inner boundary approaches the Earth to a distance of about 500 km. The outer radiation belt begins at a distance of 10,000 to 15,000 km from the Earth. The precise origin of the particles forming these belts is still not certain. Processes connected with cosmic rays reaching the Earth from outer space, and the streams of plasma ejected by the Sun during the solar flares, are probably responsible for these particles. The charged particles in the radiation belts execute a motion in the Earth's magnetic field which is of the form illustrated in Fig. 20.[4] For the sake of clarity,

[4]The trajectory shown in this figure represents the path of a high-energy ion.

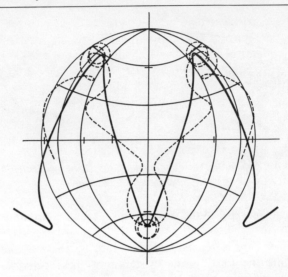

FIGURE 20. *Schematic representation of the trajectory of a charged particle in the earth's magnetic field.*

the Larmor rotation is indicated by the broken line, while the solid line represents the "axis" of the trajectory, that is, the motion of the center of the Larmor circle. An electron or ion moving in the Earth's magnetic field is therefore expected to be reflected at the magnetic poles, where the field strength is highest, and will therefore execute an oscillatory motion between the magnetic poles. In addition, there is a drift due to the nonuniform nature of the field. In view of the above analysis, this drift should give rise to a displacement of the particles in a direction perpendicular to the magnetic meridians, that is, from East to West in the case of electrons and from West to East in the case of ions. Each particle will travel around the globe while at the same time executing a rotational motion about the magnetic axis of the Earth. The lifetime of the individual electron or proton in this gigantic magnetic trap is not infinite. In the inner radiation belt, the only significant particle losses are due to collisions with atoms in the outer layers of the Earth's atmosphere. In the outer radiation belt, charged particles may be lost as a result of changes in the geometric structure of the Earth's magnetic field, that is, in the form of the lines of force. These changes occur whenever a large mass of ionized gas, ejected by the Sun during a short-period flare, reaches the Earth's neighborhood. In the case of the radiation belts, we are dealing with a rather special form of plasma which occupies an enormous volume. In point of fact, it follows from Equation (1.3) that for linear dimensions of the order of 10,000 km and particle energies of the order of 10^6 eV, an ensemble of electrons and ions will assume typical plasma properties at concentrations as low as one fast particle per cubic meter. The true density of fast electrons or protons in the radiation belts is higher than this figure by at least several orders of magnitude and this means that the Debye radius should not exceed 1,000 km.

2.7   Motion of Particles in the Presence of Electric and Magnetic Fields

Consider now some special cases of the motion of charged particles in combined electric and magnetic fields. To begin with, let us suppose that both the magnetic and the electric fields are uniform. If the electric field is parallel to the magnetic field, it will accelerate or decelerate the particle independently of the magnetic field. At the same time, the motion of the particle in the plane perpendicular to H will be unaffected by the presence of the longitudinal electric field. It follows that under these conditions the particle trajectory will be either a gradually extending or gradually contracting helix (depending on the relative directions of the electric field and the initial longitudinal velocity component). This is illustrated in Fig. 21.

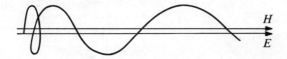

FIGURE 21. *Motion of a charged particle in parallel electric and magnetic fields.*

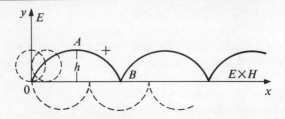

FIGURE 22. *Motion of a charged particle in crossed fields. The magnetic field is at right angles to the plane of the drawing, the electric field is in the upward direction. The trajectory is a cycloid.*

The situation is quite different when H is perpendicular to E. Suppose that at some initial instant of time the particle is at the point 0 (Fig. 22) and its velocity is equal to zero. Under the action of the electric field it will be accelerated in the direction of the y axis. (In order to be specific, we are assuming that the particle is positively charged.) The force acting on the particle due to the magnetic field will increase with increasing velocity, since the force is proportional to the velocity. This force will deflect the particle toward the x axis. The gradual curving of the trajectory should eventually give rise to a reverse motion in which the particle will move in the direction of the negative y axis. This occurs at the point A in Fig. 22. Between A and B the particle will be retarded by the electric field and the velocity will become equal to zero when the particle returns to the x axis. The acceleration process will then begin again and the whole cycle will be repeated indefinitely.

Therefore, the trajectory of the particle will consist of periodically repeating, identical arcs. Each arc is identical in form with the well-known curve called the *cycloid*. Calculations show that the height of the cycloid is $h = 2mc^2E/qH^2$, while the time taken by the particle to complete one cycloid loop is $2\pi mc/qH$; that is, it is equal to the Larmor period. A negatively charged particle will also follow a path consisting of repeated cycloids (see the broken curve in Fig. 22). We note that the direction of displacement along the axis is the same for particles of either charge.

Cycloidal trajectories of this type have long been known in

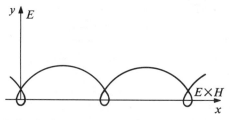

FIGURE 23. *Trochoidal motion of particles in crossed fields.*

mechanics. In fact, the cycloid is the path described by a point on the wheel of a railway wagon as it moves along the track without slipping. This analogy suggests that the motion of a charged particle in perpendicular electric and magnetic fields can also be resolved into rotational and translational motion. In point of fact, it is easy to show that the motion of an ion or an electron along a cycloid can be resolved into a rotation on a circle of radius $\frac{1}{2}h$ and a translation along the x axis with velocity cE/H. The velocity v of this translational motion is the same for all particles whatever their mass and charge. It is perpendicular both to **E** and **H** and is therefore parallel to **E** × **H**. This result may be generalized by considering the motion of a particle which starts off with a certain initial velocity v_0. Detailed calculations show that, in the more general case, the particle will travel on a trajectory which is one of the family of curves illustrated in Fig. 23 and known as *trochoids*. The trochoidal motion can also be resolved into a rotation and translation along the x axis, and it turns out that the velocity of the translational motion is always equal to cE/H. Therefore, in crossed, that is, mutually perpendicular, electric and magnetic fields, a charged particle undergoes both a helical motion under the action of H and an electric drift at right-angles to the magnetic lines of force.

Usually, the electric field both in laboratory experiments and in nature is so small that the rotational Larmor velocity of the particles is much greater than the drift velocity. The effect of the transverse electric field on the energy of the particle can then be neglected, and therefore the adiabatic invariance of $v_\perp^2/H$ remains valid even when the particles move in crossed electric and magnetic fields. If the magnetic field is not strictly uniform, then in addition to the electric drift there should also be a drift due to the variation in H. The resultant drift velocity will, of course, be equal to the sum of the two drift velocities. It should be noted that the drift which is found to take place in crossed fields is a special case of a more general law, according to which any constant force acting on a charged particle in the direction perpendicular to H gives rise to a drift at right angles to the magnetic lines of force. The direction of this motion is perpendicular to the force acting on the particle. The magnitude of the drift velocity is equal to cF/qH, where F is the force and q is the charge of the particle.[5] If the force F has the same direction both for ions and electrons, then their drift velocities will be opposite to each other. Fig. 24 shows the drift of charged particles in the gravitational field of the earth in the case where the magnetic field is parallel to the earth's surface. Although the ion drift velocity is much greater than the electron drift velocity, the absolute magnitude of the former is still quite small, even for heavy ions. In a magnetic field of 1 Oe, the drift velocity of a singly charged molecular ion of oxygen is about 3 cm per sec.

A further possible situation occurs when the magnetic field varies both in space and in time. We shall consider two simple examples of the motion of ions and electrons in variable magnetic fields. These examples will illustrate certain general regularities.

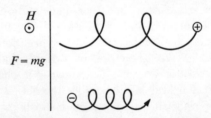

FIGURE 24. *Drift of charged particles in a gravitational field perpendicular to H.*

[5]This expression for the drift velocity can be easily derived if it is recalled that the effect of a force F on the given particle is identical with the effect of an equivalent electric field E, where $F = qE$.

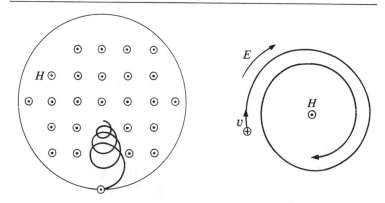

FIGURE 25a. *Motion of a charged particle in a uniform magnetic field which increases with time. The lines of force are perpendicular to the plane of the drawing.* b. *Variation in the velocity and Larmor radius due to an induced electric field.*

In the first example, the charged particle is located in a long, cylindrical chamber inside a solenoid producing a uniform magnetic field (Fig. 25a). Suppose that this field increases with time, and the problem is to determine the motion of the particle. The first point to note is that, in accordance with the law of induction, an electric field is necessarily associated with a time dependent magnetic field. The lines of this induced electric field will in the present example take the form of concentric circles, whose centers lie on the axis of the chamber. It is possible to show from the law of induction that the electric field strength E is proportional to the distance from the axis and the rate of change of H, that is, the increase in H per unit time. The electric field gives rise to a drift motion, and the drift velocity is perpendicular to both E and H, and therefore takes place in a radial direction. We can now use the various rules which we established above, in order to show that as H increases the drift occurs towards the axis, while a decreasing H is associated with an outward drift of the particles. Calculations show that as a result of the drift, the distance of the particle, or more precisely the distance of the center of its Larmor circle from the axis, is proportional to $\sqrt{H}$. However, this is not the only

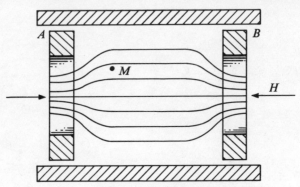

FIGURE 26. *A charged particle in the space between moving magnetic mirrors.*

effect of the induced electric field. There is also a change in $v_\perp$ and therefore in the kinetic energy of the Larmor motion. The reason for this effect can easily be established by considering the special case of a particle for which the center of the Larmor circle lies on the axis of the chamber (Fig. 25b). In this case, the induced electric field is always parallel to the rotational velocity. Therefore, it will either tend to increase the perpendicular component of the velocity or to retard the particle. The former occurs in the case of increasing H and the latter in the case of decreasing H. A quantitative analysis shows that the kinetic energy associated with the rotation of the particle is proportional to H; that is, the quantity $W_\perp/H$ is again constant. This result is valid for any particle in a variable magnetic field and can be extended to all cases involving time dependent H, provided the variation in the magnetic field is sufficiently slow.

The second example involves a charged particle with a given initial value of $v_\parallel$ trapped between two magnetic mirrors produced by the short coils A and B shown in Fig. 26. It is assumed that the field due to these coils is strong only in their immediate neighborhood and that in the region between the coils the particle moves in a relatively weak constant magnetic field produced by the long coil extending from A to B. Suppose now that the two short coils are moved towards each other. At first sight this should

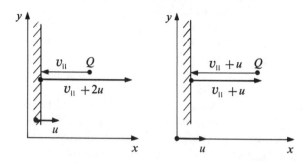

FIGURE 27. *Reflection of a mass point from a moving wall.*

merely give rise to a reduction in the region in which the longitudinal oscillations of the particle take place. However, in reality, as the coils approach each other, there is a gradual increase in the longitudinal velocity of the particles.

This increase in $v_{||}$ may be explained in two quite different ways. First, the motion of the two short coils towards each other produces a time dependent magnetic field. Thus, if at an initial time the field at the point M was H_0, then as the coils approach each other, the field will rapidly increase to a much greater value. However, the increase in H gives rise to an induced electric field which will exist near the two short coils. As the charged particle approaches the coil during its motion along the x axis it is retarded and its longitudinal component is transformed into the transverse component. The latter component also increases as a result of the effect of the electric field. This means that the total kinetic energy must increase. When the particle is reflected from the mirror, the increase in the kinetic energy associated with the transverse motion is transformed into an increase in the energy associated with the longitudinal motion, and this results in an increase in $v_{||}$. A similar result may be obtained by noting that the process involved in this particular case is analogous to the elastic reflection of a mass point from a moving wall. This will be understood from consideration of Fig. 27. On the left of this figure, the collision of a mass point Q with the wall is shown relative to the laboratory system of coordinates, whilst on the right it is shown relative to a system of coordinates which moves together with the wall. In the system of coordinates which is attached to the wall, everything occurs in accordance with the usual well-known rules: the particle is reflected and its velocity before and after the reflection is the same. Therefore, in this reference frame the particle will have a velocity $v_{||} + u$ after the collision with the wall, where u is the velocity of the wall. When the event is considered relative to the laboratory system of coordinates, it is found that the velocity of the particle moving to the left after reflection is equal to $v_{||} + 2u$; that is, it is increased by twice the velocity of the wall as compared with the initial value. One would therefore expect that the velocity of the charged particle trapped between the two magnetic mirrors discussed above will gradually increase. It may be shown that in fact $v_{||}$ will be inversely proportional to the distance between the mirrors, whatever the magnitude of H.

We thus see that under certain conditions, a time dependent magnetic field may affect both the transverse and the longitudinal velocity components of charged particles. The true physical reason for the change in the velocity is always the same, namely, the acceleration of the particles in electric fields which are always associated with time dependent magnetic fields.

The above mechanisms which are available for the acceleration of charged particles are being currently used in various experimental studies whose aim is to produce high-temperature plasma. By radially contracting the plasma with the aid of an increasing magnetic field and then compressing it with movable magnetic mirrors, we are merely copying the phenomenon which occurs on a gigantic scale in nature. It is well known that streams of particles of very high energy, known as cosmic rays, reach the earth from outer space. Even now, there is no direct experimental evidence concerning the origin of these particles. However, the fact that they have such high energies is no longer puzzling because, as we have seen, it is possible that they are accelerated during interactions with the magnetic fields of stars and nebulae as they wander through space for a very considerable time. The distinguished Italian physicist Enrico Fermi, who contributed so much to modern physics (in particular, he built the first nuclear reactor), pointed out in 1949 that cosmic ray particles may be accelerated by colliding with moving magnetic "clouds," that is, regions of space in which there are nonzero magnetic fields. Astronomical data suggest that such clouds wander randomly through the galaxy, giving rise to tangled up clusters of magnetic lines of force. When a charged particle collides with a magnetic cloud moving towards it, its energy increases. It is quite easy to show that a collision with a receding cloud gives rise to a reduction in the energy. At first sight it would appear that the two effects would cancel out. However, Fermi was able to show that a complete compensation does not, in fact, take place, and that the velocity received by a charged particle moving towards a magnetic cloud is greater than the velocity received during a recessive collision. Therefore, during its very long random motion in the interstellar space, a charged particle will gradually attain greater and greater velocity, and its energy may reach many billions of electron volts. This mechanism for the acceleration of cosmic rays, which was first put forward by Fermi, may be augmented by the induction mechanism which leads to an increase in the final velocity of particles in longitudinal fields which are increasing with time.

3

The Motion of Charged
Particles in Plasma

3.1   A General Review of the Properties of Gases

In this and in the subsequent chapters, we shall make maximum use of the analogy between a plasma and an ordinary gas. To begin with, let us recall briefly the main properties of gases. The most important parameters which characterize the physical state of a gas are the density n (the number of molecules or atoms per unit volume) and the temperature T. The mean kinetic energy of the particles depends only on the temperature [see Equation (1.2)], while the gas pressure is proportional both to the density and the temperature. This is an expression of the laws of Boyle and Gay-Lussac.

The formula relating the pressure p, the density n, and the temperature T is

$$p = nkT. \tag{3.1}$$

This equation is valid for any gas at a sufficiently high temperature, provided the density n is not too great. When the gas consists of a mixture of components with densities n_1, n_2, and so on, each of the components gives rise to its own partial pressure, and thus, for a mixture of gases, Equation (3.1) may be written in the form

$$p = p_1 + p_2 + \cdots = (n_1 + n_2 + \cdots)kT, \tag{3.2}$$

where $p_1, p_2, \ldots$ are given by

$$p_1 = n_1kT, \qquad p_2 = n_2kT, \ldots$$

It is, of course, assumed that the temperatures of the components of the gas mixture are the same. In practice, this condition is always satisfied in a neutral gas because there is a rapid energy transfer between molecules belonging to the different components.

Consider the simplest case when the gas molecules are all of the same kind. Even when the temperature of the gas is maintained at a constant value, this does not mean that all the molecules have the same velocities and therefore the same energies. On the contrary, both theoretical calculations and direct measurements show that the molecules may have very different velocities, lying between zero and very large valeus. In the middle of the nineteenth century, Maxwell showed that the number of gas molecules which have velocities lying between v and $v + \Delta v$ is given by

$$N = Av^2 e^{-mv^2/2kT} \Delta v, \tag{3.3}$$

where e is the base of natural logarithms ($e = 2.718$). The coefficient A can be determined from the condition that the total number of molecules per cubic centimetre must be equal to the density n. It is found that A is proportional to n and is a function of both the mass m of the molecules and the temperature T.[6]

The velocity distribution is illustrated in Fig. 28, in which the relative number of molecules per unit velocity interval is plotted

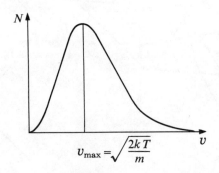

FIGURE 28. *Maxwellian velocity distribution.*

[6]The coefficient A is given by the formula $A = \sqrt{\dfrac{2}{\pi}\left(\dfrac{m}{kT}\right)^3}$.

as a function of the velocity v. A characteristic feature of this distribution is the maximum at $v = \sqrt{2kT/m}$ (this is the most probable velocity), and the very rapid decrease in the number of molecules at low velocities. Calculations show that for the Maxwellian velocity distribution the relative number of molecules having velocities in excess of five times the most probable velocity is only about $3 \times 10^{-11}\%$. The kinetic energy distribution can easily be deduced from the velocity distribution. It can be shown that the number of particles with energies between W and $W + \Delta W$ is proportional to $\sqrt{W}e^{-W/kT}\Delta W$, provided ΔW is small enough. We note that the individual properties of the molecules do not enter into the expression for the energy distribution, and therefore the energy distribution will be the same for all the components of a mixture.

If we confine our attention to one of the molecules of the gas and follow it in its random thermal motion, we shall find that its path will take the zig-zag form illustrated in Fig. 29. Each break in this curve is the result of an elastic collision of the particular molecule with some other molecule of the gas. The dur-

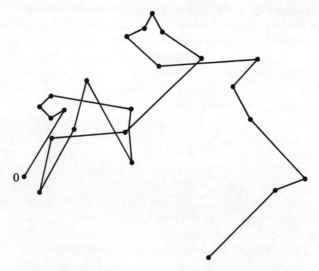

FIGURE 29. *Brownian (random) motion of a gas molecule.*

ation of each collision is very small in comparison with the time between successive collisions. For the sake of simplicity we shall assume that after a collision the particle can, with equal probability, continue in any direction, irrespective of its initial direction of motion. The elementary kinetic theory of gases, which provides an explanation of most properties of gases, is based on this simple assumption. We shall now examine the various concepts used in this theory which, in a somewhat modified form, are widely used in plasma physics.

The mean length of the straight-line sections making up the zig-zag path of the molecules in the gas is known as the *mean free path* of the molecule, and is usually denoted by λ. The average time taken by a molecule to traverse these straight-line sections is known as the mean-time between collisions and is usually denoted by τ. The mean collision frequency, that is, the average number of collisions experienced by the particle per second, is then $1/\tau$ and is denoted by ν. The parameters λ, τ, and ν can be related to the characteristics which determine the collision process between the molecules by introducing the concept of the *effective collision cross section*. The effective collision cross section has a simple geometric interpretation. A collision will occur only if the centers of the colliding molecules are at a certain minimum distance from each other. For example, if the molecules behave as if they were rigid spheres of radii a, collisions will occur when the distance between the centers is less than $2a$. This quantity is called the effective collision radius and the quantity $4\pi a^2$ is called the effective collision cross section. We shall denote it by σ. The idea of an effective collision cross section is useful because it leads to the following interpretation: A collision may be regarded as the impact of a molecule on a target of definite dimensions. The larger the target, that is, the larger the magnitude of $4\pi a^2$, the more frequent the collisions between the molecules, and the smaller the mean free path (other things being equal). It is evident that the mean free path λ will also depend on the density of the molecules. Thus, the larger the density n, that is, the larger the number of molecules per unit volume, the smaller the magnitude of λ. The algebraic relation between the effective collision cross section and

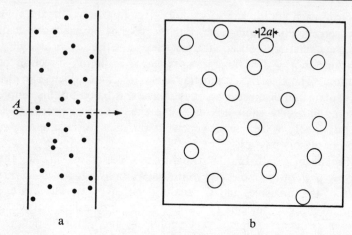

FIGURE 30. *Passage of a molecule through a thin layer of gas:* a. *lateral view,* b. *front view (molecule moving into the plane of the paper).*

the mean free path can be derived by considering Fig. 30a. This figure shows the passage of a molecule A through a very thin layer of gas which we can imagine as existing in space. The path of the molecule is indicated by the dashed line. It is perpendicular to the surfaces of the layer. In order to simplify the calculations, let us suppose that all the molecules in the layer, except for the molecule A, whose fate we are investigating, are at rest. If the thickness of the layer d is sufficiently small, the probability that the collision will occur is d/λ. Thus, for example, when $d/\lambda = 0.01$, only one out of a hundred molecules passing through the layer will, on the average, experience a collision within this layer.

On the other hand, the probability of a collision depends on the number of molecules in the layer and on the magnitude of the effective collision cross section σ. Fig. 30b shows the gas layer as seen by the incident molecule A. Circles of diameter $2a$ are drawn around each of the target molecules. Whenever an incident molecule enters one of these circles we say that a collision has taken place. In order to determine the probability of a collision of this kind, we must find the relative area occupied by these targets Suppose that the area of the layer shown in Fig. 30b is S so that the volume occupied by the layer is *Sd*. The total number of molecules in the layer is *nSd* and the total area occupied by the target circles is $nSd\sigma$. The ratio of this area to the total area of the layer *S* is, in fact, the required collision probability, which is therefore equal to $nd\sigma$. However, it was shown above that this probability is also d/λ. Therefore $d/\lambda = nd\sigma$ and hence

$$\lambda = \frac{1}{n\sigma}. \tag{3.4}$$

This expression was derived on the assumption that all the molecules but one are at rest. This assumption is clearly invalid and the above formula must be corrected for the fact that the target molecules are also in motion. If it is assumed that all the molecules behave as if they were perfectly rigid spheres, then the expression relating λ, *n*, and σ is found to be

$$\lambda = \frac{1}{\sqrt{2}} \cdot \frac{1}{n\sigma}. \tag{3.5}$$

Thus, when the motion of the molecules is taken into account, the mean free path is reduced by a factor of about 1.4. The mean time between successive collisions can then be found from

$$\tau = \frac{\lambda}{\bar{v}}. \tag{3.6}$$

where $\bar{v}$ is the mean velocity of the molecules which is very nearly equal to the most probable velocity.[7]

The mean number of collisions which a molecule experiences per second is equal to $\bar{v}/\lambda$. If all other molecules are assumed to be at rest, then

$$\nu = n\bar{v}\sigma. \tag{3.7}$$

When the motion of the target molecules is taken into account, this formula will include an additional factor of $\sqrt{2}$. For a gas

[7]This is not quite true since the mean of a quotient is not equal to the quotient of the means. However, this mathematical distinction is not of particular importance in the present context.

consisting of neutral atoms and molecules, the cross section σ can, to a first approximation, be taken as constant, that is, independent of velocity. It follows that the mean free path λ is also independent of velocity and therefore of temperature, and varies only with the density n. Table 1 gives some typical values for the parameters σ and λ. In the case of nonatomic gases, for example, helium or argon, the collision frequency and the mean free path refer to collisions between atoms. In the case of molecular gases (hydrogen, nitrogen, oxygen) these parameters refer to collisions between molecules. The mean free paths are given for $n = 3.5 \times 10^{16}$ particles per cm^3 which corresponds to a pressure of 1mm Hg at room temperature ($T = 300°K$).

TABLE 1

Gas	σ (cm^2)	$\lambda(\times 10^{-3}cm)$
hydrogen	$2.4 \cdot 10^{-15}$	8.4
helium	$1.5 \cdot 10^{-15}$	13.5
oxygen	$4.1 \cdot 10^{-15}$	5.0
nitrogen	$4.4 \cdot 10^{-16}$	4.6
argon	$4.2 \cdot 10^{-16}$	4.8

3.2 Collisions between Charged Particles in Plasma

After this brief review of the behavior of atoms and molecules in a neutral gas, let us proceed to the laws governing the motion of ions and electrons in plasma which, by definition, is a gas consisting (if only partly) of charged particles. It seems quite natural to discuss the effects of the interactions between the electrons and ions on the nature of their motion in terms of the concepts which have been so successful in the conventional kinetic theory of gases. In particular, this means that we can use the concepts of the effective collision cross section, mean free path, and so on. However, in the case of plasma the use of these parameters leads to certain difficulties which are directly connected with the particular nature of the interaction between the plasma particles. In contrast to the forces acting between neutral molecules, which have a very short range of action and become appreciable only when the particles approach each other to within 10^{-8} to 10^{-7}cm, the Coulomb forces between the ions and electrons have a very long range and are appreciable even at large distances. (They are inversely proportional to the square of the distance.) Therefore, the path of an ion or an electron in plasma will be quite different from the zig-zag curve shown in Fig. 29. The path of a charged particle in a highly ionized plasma, in which the electrostatic interaction between the particles is the most important interaction, cannot be resolved into straight line sections which begin and end at the points at which the collisions take place. In plasma, each individual particle is always in the field due to the remaining electrons and ions, which is subject to continuous fluctuations both in magnitude and direction (see Fig. 2). This plasma microfield gives rise to a continuous variation in the magnitude and direction of the velocity of a charged particle in the plasma; and this variation takes place continuously since the intensity of the microfield is on the average quite small.

The order of magnitude of the microfield E can easily be estimated as follows:

If it is assumed that the ions are singly charged, then the total number of charged particles of both signs in a cubic centimetre is $2n_e$, where n_e is the number of electrons per cm³. Therefore, the volume occupied by a single particle is $1/2n_e$, and the mean distance between neighboring particles is equal to $1/\sqrt[3]{2n_e}$. The field at a point halfway between the particles, that is, at a distance $1/2\sqrt[3]{2n_e}$ from one of the electrons or ions in the plasma, can be taken as a measure of the intensity of the microfield. From this, it can be shown that the mean intensity E of the internal electric field is of the order of $e/r^2 \approx 6en_e^{2/3}$. More rigorous calculations show that the mean field is of the order of $20en_e^{2/3}$.

Because the changes in the direction of the velocities are statistical in nature, the trajectory of the particle will resemble the random

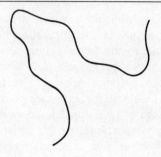

FIGURE 31. *Trajectory of a charged particle in plasma.*

walk of a person lost in a desert at night. A trajectory of this kind is illustrated in Fig. 31.

We shall now try to analyze the motion of particles in a plasma in terms of the known two-body interactions between the particles. We shall try to show that the gradual change in the direction of the velocity is the result of a large number of very weak interactions. These interactions occur through the electrostatic field acting between the particles. The angular deflection ϑ experienced by an electron or an ion in an elementary collision is given by Equation (2.5) provided ϑ is not too large. It follows from this equation that the scattering angle is inversely proportional to the impact parameter b. In order that the particle should be deflected through an angle greater than ϑ it must strike the scattering center within an area of radius b. The area of this circle is πb^2 and is inversely proportional to ϑ^2. It follows that collisions giving rise to large scattering angles have a very low probability, while small angles of deflection occur very frequently. A detailed theoretical analysis shows that it is these very frequent small deflections which combine in accordance with statistical laws to give rise to the gradual variation in the direction of the moving particle as illustrated in Fig. 31.

One further point is worth noting here. Since the plasma contains charged particles of two kinds, namely, electrons and ions, there are, in fact, three kinds of electrostatic interactions: electron-electron, electron-ion, and ion-ion interactions. In this chapter we shall be interested mainly in the behavior of the plasma electrons. The motion of each electron is affected both by the Coulomb field due to the ions and the Coulomb field due to the other electrons. Both interactions play an approximately equal part in the continuous variation in the direction of the velocity of an electron during its motion. It is not possible to determine, from a consideration of the trajectory of an electron, which of the two interactions is responsible for any particular small deflection. However, it will be seen later that, in many plasma processes, the electron-ion and the electron-electron interactions play quite different roles. It will therefore be useful to discuss the two interactions separately. The electron-ion interaction will be characterized by the quantity τ_{ei} which can be formally defined as the mean interval of time between successive collisions between electrons and ions. This definition may be justified as follows: Suppose, for the moment, that the plasma consists of ions only, except for a test electron executing a random motion in the space occupied by the positive ions. The test electron will start its motion in a certain definite direction. After a small number of successive deflections in the electric fields of the ions, the test electron will "forget" its original direction of motion. Roughly speaking, this means that the direction of its velocity will be deflected through an angle of the order of 90°. The average time which is necessary for this to happen is the quantity τ_{ei}. The mean time between electron-electron collisions can be defined in a similar way by ignoring the collisions with the ions. We shall denote this quantity by τ_{ee}. It must also be remembered that, when the plasma is not fully ionized, the electrons will also experience collisions with the neutral atoms. These can be characterized by τ_{e0} which can be defined in analogy with τ_{ei}. The quantity τ_e, which represents all interactions and is therefore the mean interval of time between successive collisions experienced by an electron in the plasma, can be expressed in terms of τ_{ei}, τ_{ee}, and τ_{e0} and is given by

$$\frac{1}{\tau_e} = \frac{1}{\tau_{ei}} + \frac{1}{\tau_{ee}} + \frac{1}{\tau_{e0}}. \tag{3.8}$$

In point of fact, $1/\tau_e = \nu_e$ is the total number of "collisions" undergone by the electron per second, and must clearly be equal to the sum of the electron-ion, ($\nu_{ei} = 1/\tau_{ei}$), electron-electron ($\nu_{ee} = 1/\tau_{ee}$) and electron-atom ($\nu_{e0} = 1/\tau_{e0}$) collisions per second. The concept of the mean free path can also be used to describe the motion of electrons in plasma. It is defined as the distance of motion necessary for memory of the intial direction of motion of the electron to be lost. The mean free path λ_e and the mean time τ_e are related by $\lambda_e = \bar{v}_e \tau_e$, where $\bar{v}_e$ is the mean thermal velocity of the electrons. In addition, it is possible to introduce the quantities λ_{ei}, λ_{ee}, and λ_{e0} which characterize the mean free paths of the electrons with respect to the various forms of interaction.

The next step in our analogy between plasma processes and the kinetic theory of gases should be the introduction of the concept of an effective Coulomb collision cross section. As before, we must distinguish between electron-ion, electron-electron, and electron neutral atom interactions, that is, we must distinguish between the cross sections σ_{ei}, σ_{ee}, and σ_{e0}. It must be recalled that each of these is used to replace the effect of a large number of small deflections by a single "collision" which is analogous to a collision between two spheres. The derivation of the expressions for the effective cross sections is beyond the scope of this book, but it will be useful to discuss certain approximate ideas which will provide us with an insight into the exact expressions.

According to Equation (2.8) the impact parameter corresponding to a collision between two charged particles, in which the velocity vector of one of the particles is turned through 90°, is given by

$$b_0 = \frac{q_1 q_1}{m_1 v_1^2}. \tag{3.9}$$

where the subscript $_1$ refers to the particle which has been scattered through 90°. For the sake of simplicity we shall suppose that the other charged particle (represented by the subscript $_2$) has a much greater mass and simply acts as a center of the electrostatic force. Let us draw a circle of radius b_0 about this center. Its area will be $S = (q_1 q_2/m_1 v_1^2)^2$. If we set $q_1 = e$ and $q_2 = Ze$, then

$$S = \pi \frac{Z^2 e^4}{m_1^2 v_1^4}. \tag{3.10}$$

The area given by this expression can be interpreted as the effective electron-ion interaction cross section if m_1 and v_1 represent the mass and the velocity of the plasma electron respectively, and Z represents the number of elementary charges carried by the ion. This expression was derived on the assumption that distant encounters corresponding to large impact parameters, in which the electron is deflected through very small angles, can be ignored. However, detailed analysis shows that in reality the overall effect of these small deflections is much greater than the effect of the rare close encounters in which there is a sudden change in the direction of motion of the electron. The reason for this is that the weak interactions are much more frequent than the strong interactions. It follows that Equation (3.10) is, in fact, an underestimate of the effective cross section. Exact calculations show that the true cross section is greater by an order of magnitude as compared with Equation (3.10).[8] In approximate calculations using σ_{ei} one can use the expression

$$\sigma_{ei} \approx \frac{4 \cdot 10^{-5} \cdot Z_i^2}{T_e^2}, \tag{3.11}$$

which gives the mean value of σ_{ei} taking into account the fact that the electron velocities are not equal, but are distributed in accordance with Maxwell's law. This is the reason why the denominator involves the square of the electron temperature. The expression for σ_{ee} is analogous in form:

$$\sigma_{ee} \approx 6 \cdot 10^{-5} \cdot \frac{1}{T_e^2}. \tag{3.12}$$

The mean free path for electron-ion collisions is related to σ_{ei} by an expression which is analogous to (3.4):

$$\lambda_{ei} \approx \frac{2.5 \cdot 10^4 T_e^2}{Z^2 n}. \tag{3.13}$$

Moreover,

$$\tau_{ei} \approx \frac{4 \cdot 10^{-2} T_e^{3/2}}{Z_i^2 n_i}, \qquad \nu_{ei} \approx 25 \cdot \frac{n_i Z_i^2}{T_e^{3/2}}. \tag{3.14}$$

[8]However, the energy dependence of the effective cross section is given correctly by Equation (3.10).

The symbol $\approx$ in these formulas indicates their approximate nature.

The interaction between charged particles in plasma can therefore be described within the framework of the ordinary kinetic theory of gases by replacing the continuously varying trajectories of the electrons by certain conventional broken lines, and by combining the statistical effect of a large number of weak interactions into one strong interaction. The advantage of this not very rigorous analysis is that Equations (3.11)–(3.14) provide a convenient conceptual picture of what happens in a plasma in which the electrons and ions are ascribed properties analogous to those of ordinary billiard balls.

Moreover, the formulas given above exhibit the most important properties which characterize the behavior of the constituent particles in plasma. In particular, it is evident that the cross sections σ_{ei} and σ_{ee} decrease rapidly with increasing electron temperature. A few specific examples will show the relative importance of the Coulomb interactions in cold and hot plasma. Suppose that $n_i = 10^{14}$ particles per cm³ and $Z = 1$. These numbers correspond to a hydrogen plasma of very high density. At $T_e = 10,000°K$, which corresponds to a mean electron energy of about 1.5eV, Equations (3.11), (3.13), and (3.14) yield

$$\sigma_{ei} \approx 4 \cdot 10^{-13} \text{ cm}^2$$
$$\lambda_{ei} \approx 0.03 \text{ cm}$$
$$\tau_{ei} \approx 4 \cdot 10^{-10} \text{ sec}$$
$$\nu_{ei} \approx 2.5 \cdot 10^9 \text{ sec}^{-1}.$$

When $T_e = 10^8°K$, which is the goal of physicists concerned with controlled thermonuclear reactions, the corresponding values are

$$\sigma_{ei} \approx 4 \cdot 10^{-21} \text{ cm}^2$$
$$\lambda_{ei} \approx 3 \cdot 10^6 \text{ cm}$$
$$\tau_{ei} \approx 4 \cdot 10^{-4} \text{ sec}$$
$$\nu_{ei} \approx 2.5 \cdot 10^3 \text{ sec}^{-1}.$$

Comparison of these special cases will show the very considerable effect which a change in the temperature of the plasma has on the collisions between the charged particles. Thus, in a low-temperature plasma (we shall not refer to matter at a temperature of 10,000°K as *cold* plasma), the electron experiences about ten collisions per centimetre, while in a plasma at a temperature of 10^8°K, and with the same density, the electron will traverse tens of kilometers without experiencing any appreciable interaction with its numerous neighbors. This means that the Coulomb interactions can be practically ignored in the case of a high-temperature plasma.

The interaction between the charged particles leads not only to a change in the direction of their velocities, but also to energy transfer between them. Suppose, for example, that a fast particle having a large kinetic energy passes by another parricle which may be regarded as the center of force (Fig. 32). As a result of the encounter between the two bodies, the incident particle experiences a small deflection. This means that there is a change in the angular momentum (moment of momentum) of the incident particle. According to the basic laws of mechanics, the total angular momentum of a system of two interacting charges must remain the same before and after the collision. Therefore, the second particle, which acts as the center of force, will receive an impulse in the direction indicated by the arrow in the figure, and will be given a velocity v_3; that is, a fraction of the kinetic energy of the incident fast particle will be transferred to the target particle. This fraction will increase with decreasing distance between the particles and decreasing mass of the particle to which the energy is transmitted, so that for a given impulse, the energy given to the second particle is inversely proportional to its mass.[9] Therefore, for the same initial energy, a fast ion will transfer to an electron

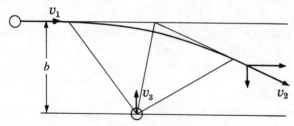

FIGURE 32. *Collision of a fast particle with a target particle at rest: v_1 and v_2 are the velocities of the fast particle before and after the collision; v_3 is the velocity of the target particle after the collision.*

[9]Since the kinetic energy is given by $W = \frac{1}{2}mv^2$ and the momentum by $p = mv$, it follows that $W = p^2/2m$.

at rest much more energy than a fast electron will transfer to an
ion at rest. An electron with kinetic energy considerably greater
than the mean kinetic energy of the ions surrounding it, will
traverse a very long path and will change its direction of motion a
great many times before it gives up its energy to the ions. The
amount of energy which is transferred from a fast electron to the
ions per unit time decreases with increasing velocity of the electron.
This is explained by the fact that, in accordance with Equation
(2.5), the angle of deflection decreases rapidly with increasing
velocity of the incident particle, and therefore there is a rapid
decrease in the amount of transferred momentum. Calculations
show that the energy lost by a fast electron of energy W per unit
time to the plasma ions is given by

$$Q \approx 1.3 \cdot 10^{-25} \frac{n_i Z^2}{A \sqrt{W}}, \qquad (3.15)$$

where n_i is the ion concentration, Z is the number of elementary
charges per ion, and A is their atomic weight. It is assumed that
the ions may be regarded as being at rest; that is, the thermal
energy of the ions is very small in comparison with the electron
energy. In plasma, the various physical processes usually proceed
so that the energy taken from external sources is given to the
electrons, and some of it is then transferred from the electrons to
the ions. Therefore, the electron temperature T_e will be much
higher than the ion temperature T_i. In order to estimate the rate
of thermal energy transfer from the electrons to the ions, we can
use Equation (3.15) and replace W by the mean thermal energy of
the electrons. The quantity $n_e Q$ is then equal to the amount of
energy transferred in one cubic centimetre per second from the
electrons to the ions. If T_e and T_i are comparable, then the energy
transfer is smaller in the ratio of $T_e - T_i$ to T_e.

Consider now some numerical examples characterizing the
transfer of thermal energy from the electrons to the ions in a
hydrogen plasma. Suppose that $n = 10^{13}$ particles per cm³,
$T_e = 10^5 °$K, and $T_i = 0$. The amount of energy received per second

per cubic centimetre by the ions from the electrons is then equal to 4×10^6 erg, which corresponds to a power transfer of 0.4 kilowatts per litre. Suppose now that the external source of energy is switched off, so that after a short interval of time a virtually complete thermal equilibrium is established between the electrons and the ions, and T_i is practically equal to T_e. In point of fact, with the above rate of heat transfer, each electron will lose on the average about 4×10^{-12} erg in 10 microseconds, which corresponds to a reduction in its temperature by 30,000°K and a corresponding increase in the temperature of the ions. Therefore T_i and T_e will become equal in only about 20 microseconds after the external source of energy is switched off. However, if the electron temperature is increased to 10^{8}°K, without a change in their concentration, the rate of heat transfer will be reduced by a factor of 30. The time necessary to establish thermal equilibrium between the electrons and the ions will then increase by a factor of 3×10^4, and will therefore be of the order of a second.

The above examples are purely illustrative. The ratio of T_e to T_i may, in general, vary within very wide limits, depending on the conditions prevailing in the plasma. In a plasma with a low density of charged particles, the heat transfer between the electrons and the ions may be very slight at relatively low electron temperatures, and therefore a hot electron gas may be mixed with a cold ion component. However, there are other possible cases when T_e and T_i may be approximately equal. For example, studies of the radiation emitted by the plasma forming the outer layer of the sun suggest that the electron and ion temperatures in this plasma are not very different.

3.3 Interaction of Electrons and Ions with Neutral Particles

A two-particle interaction, in which the total kinetic energy of the interacting particles remains the same and in which there is only a redistribution of energy between them, is called an elastic interaction. The collisions between the charged particles in plasma which we have discussed so far belong to this category. However, there are also inelastic collisions in which a fraction of the available kinetic energy is transformed into other forms of energy, for example, radiation, or the internal energy of one of the interacting particles. Inelastic collisions leading to the emission of radiation will be discussed in Chapter 4. For the moment we shall merely note that there are two main types of such processes, namely, deceleration of electrons in the electric field of the ions, which is accompanied by the emission of light or x rays, and capture of electrons by ions, which is also accompanied by the emission of radiation. Inelastic collisions of the second kind, in which the kinetic energy is transformed into internal energy of one of the particles, are analogous to the corresponding processes which occur with the participation of neutral atoms and must therefore be considered together with these processes.

A fully ionized plasma consisting of bare atomic nuclei and free electrons is a theoretical abstraction; in a real situation one has to deal with plasma containing both positive ions and neutral atoms and molecules. The number of charged particles in the plasma produced in a gas discharge tube or in the ionosphere is very small compared to the number of neutral atoms. It is only recently that almost fully ionized plasma has been produced under laboratory conditions in experimental apparatus for the production of high-temperature plasma. Therefore, the interaction between charged and neutral particles may play an important part in many physical phenomena which are encountered in plasma. In particular, when the density of charged particles is relatively low, the motion of these particles will be affected to a greater extent by collisions with neutral atoms or molecules than by collisions with other charged particles. Among the various possible interactions between the neutral particles on the one hand and the electrons and ions on the other, the most important from the point of view of plasma physics are the interactions with electrons. An electron colliding with a neutral atom may undergo elastic scattering, which is accompanied by a change in its direction of motion and by a small loss of energy. However, there are also collisions in which the atom is ionized or excited; that is, it is raised to a higher energy level. To each of these processes can be ascribed an effective cross section. As before, the effective cross section is a measure of the strength of the interaction, and can be used to replace a complicated set of true collision processes by a simple model involving an incident particle and randomly distributed spherical targets.

The effective cross section for the collision of an electron with an atom, whether it be the elastic cross section or the cross section for ionization or excitation, is very dependent both on the energy of the electron and on the chemical properties of the target atom.

Figure 33 shows the effective cross section σ_s for elastic scattering of electrons by hydrogen molecules, and helium molecules, argon and krypton atoms as a function of the electron energy. In all cases there is a decrease in σ_s with increasing electron energy W provided W is high enough. At energies below 10 eV the dependence of σ_s on W may be quite complicated. For example, the noble gases are characterized by a minimum in σ_s at low values of W. These minima are responsible for a very considerable reduction

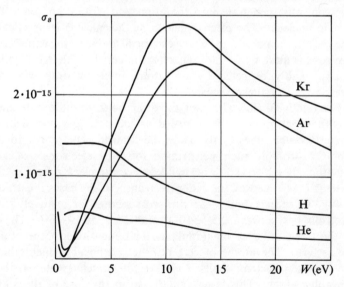

FIGURE 33. *Elastic scattering cross section of electrons by different gases as a function of the electron energy in electron-volts.*

in the interactions between electrons and atoms in a very narrow range of energies. This phenomenon is known as the Ramsauer effect. It is due to the fact that the electrons have associated wave properties. Under certain conditions, when the ratio of the wavelength of the moving electron to the linear dimensions of the atom is a favorable value, the wave can pass directly through the atom. (This is analogous to the interference effects which are observed during the passage of light through thin films.) We shall not go into the details of these wave effects, but will simply regard them as an experimental fact.

The reduction in the magnitude of σ_s at high energies can easily be explained. It is due to the fact that an increase in the velocity leads to a reduction in the time of interaction, which always tends to reduce the effect due to the collision. This is a general property of elastic collisions. At very high electron energies, the collision of an electron with a neutral atom is not very different from a collision with an ion, since in order to undergo a large deflection, the electron must penetrate into the atom and closely approach the atomic nucleus. The electric field near the nucleus is practically due only to the nucleus itself; the electric field due to the extraneous electrons is quite negligible. Therefore, a very fast electron, which is appreciably deflected by the atom, interacts only with the electric field of the nucleus.

For relatively slow electrons the atom behaves quite differently and the electron must be regarded as interacting with a field of force which becomes so strong, as the electron penetrates into the atom to prohibit such penetration for slow electrons. Outside the atom these forces are negligible, since the electric field of the nucleus is screened by the outer electrons. In the cases illustrated in Fig. 33, the maximum effective cross section for relatively slow electrons lies between 0.5×10^{-15} and 2.5×10^{-15} cm^2. This is of the same order of magnitude as the dimensions of the atoms themselves. The atoms of certain other chemical elements have much larger electron shells, and therefore much greater σ_s than the noble gases. This is particularly so in the case of the alkali metals. Thus, for example, the maximum value of σ_s for cesium is 5×10^{-14} cm^2.

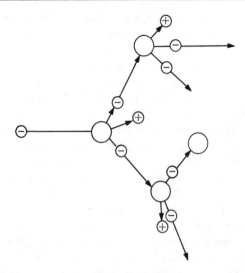

FIGURE 34. *Cascade process during the ionization of a gas.*

The scattering of an electron by an atom gives rise to a very small energy transfer, just as in the case of the Coulomb, or electrostatic interaction between an electron and an ion. The mean energy transfer is of the order of $(2m_e/m_a)W$, where m_a is the mass of the atom. Therefore, when an electron of energy equal to 1 eV collides with an oxygen atom whose mass is greater than m_e by a factor of about 30000, the energy transferred to the atom is less than 10^{-4} eV. This is smaller by a factor of about 300 than the thermal energy of the oxygen atom at room temperature.

Among the various forms of inelastic interaction between electrons and atoms, the most important for most plasma phenomena are those which give rise to the ionization of the atoms. Each ionizing event gives rise to the appearance of a new pair of charged particles (Fig. 34). It is precisely as a result of such processes, leading to the cascade development of a gas discharge, that plasma is usually formed. A definite amount of energy W_i must be spent in removing an electron from an atom. This energy is known as the ionization energy and is usually expressed in electron volts. It is also frequently referred to as the ionizaton potential, which is numerically equal to the ionization energy W_i, but is expressed simply in volts. Thus, for example, the ionization energy of the hydrogen atom is 13.6 eV and therefore the ionization potential of hydrogen is said to be 13.6 V. This terminology is convenient because it indicates immediately the minimum potential difference through which an electron must fall before it is capable of ionizing a given atom. An electron which has fallen through a potential difference smaller than 13.6 V will not succeed in ionizing a hydrogen atom. If the energy of the electron incident on a neutral atom is greater than the ionization energy, then the surplus energy $W - W_i$ is shared between the two electrons, that is, the primary electron and the electron leaving the atom.

In particular, when W is much greater than W_i, the most probable processes are those in which the secondary electron is given relatively little energy (of the order of W_i). This can be easily explained. A fast electron flying past one of the atomic electrons transmits to it a very small momentum, and therefore a small amount of energy. If the transmitted energy in this almost elastic collision is greater than W_i, then ionization will take place, and a low energy free electron is produced. If, however, W is only slightly greater than W_i, then the two electrons are indistinguishable, and their energies are roughly the same.

Since, in general, an atom other than hydrogen and its isotopes, deuterium and tritium, has more than one electron, and each of them is bound in a different way to the nucleus, a number of different ionization potentials must be ascribed to a given atom. The minimum ionization potential gives the energy necessary to remove the outermost electrons. These are the valence electrons, which determine the chemical properties of the atom and many of its important physical properties, for example, the geometric dimensions, some of the magnetic properties, the spectral composition of the emitted radiation, and so on.

Table 2 lists the minimum ionization potentials of a number of elements. As can be seen, the smallest ionization potential occurs in cesium — an alkali metal — while in the noble gases, whose valence electrons form closed shells, the ionization potential is quite high.

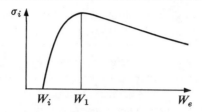

FIGURE 35. *Typical variation of the ionization cross section with electron energy.*

TABLE 2

Element	W_i (eV)	Element	W_i (eV)
hydrogen	13.54	argon	15.68
helium	24.48	iron	7.83
nitrogen	14.51	cesium	3.86
oxygen	13.57		

The ionization potentials corresponding to the removal of inner electrons are much greater than the minimum ionization potentials given in Table 2. In the case of heavy atoms, they may reach the order of 10^4 V or more (such electrons are located nearer to the atomic nucleus and are therefore more strongly bound to it).

Figure 35 shows a typical variation of the effective ionization cross section of an atom with the energy of the incident electron. The cross section is zero at $W = W_i$, where W_i is the ionization potential for the most loosely bound valence electron. The cross section then increases rapidly and reaches a maximum at $W = W_1$, which lies between 40 and 80 eV, the position depending on the particular element. As the energy is increased still further, it is found that σ_i decreases at first slowly and then more rapidly. This form of the ionization curve may be explained in terms of the ideas which we have previously discussed. As long as the energy of the incident electron is low, it must approach a bound electron very closely before it can give up to the bound electron an energy which is sufficient for ionization to occur. Therefore, with increasing W, the value of the impact parameter b for which ionization is possible should also increase.

For very fast electrons there is a further important factor, namely, the interaction is effectively reduced because it takes place in a very short interval of time. This is the same factor which is responsible for the reduction in the heat transfer between the particles (see above). Therefore, it is not surprising that very fast electrons have a low ionizing efficiency. The maximum value of σ_i is different for different elements: It varies between 0.7×10^{-16} cm^2 (hydrogen) and 6×10^{-16} cm^2 (heavy elements, for example, mercury). We note that the curve shown in Fig. 35 summarizes all the properties of ionization processes; that is, it includes both the removal of the valence electrons from outer surface of the atom and the removal of electrons belonging to the inner shells. In fact, however, the contribution due to the internal electrons to the effective ionization cross section is small provided W is not too high. The probability that an electron colliding with an atom will eject one of the inner electrons is small in comparison with the probability of removing a valence electron. It is difficult therefore to say what part of the total ionization curve is due to strong interactions giving rise to the ejection of inner electrons.

The incident ionizing electron will not only lose energy, but will also undergo a change in its direction of motion, and this change increases with increasing proportion of transferred energy. In this respect, the ionization process is analogous to the scattering of electrons by neutral atoms. However, the role of ionizing events in the energy balance of a fast electron moving in matter is very much greater than the role of elastic scattering by neutral atoms, since for ionizing events the electron loses a large proportion of its energy instantaneously, while in elastic collisions the energy loss is quite negligible.

So far, we have been concerned with the individual ionizing events involving the collision between an electron of given initial energy and an atom. In order to evaluate the ionization processes in plasma, it must be remembered that the plasma electrons have different energies. An individual electron will produce $n_0\sigma_i$ ions per centimetre of its path, where n_0 is the neutral particle density.

Since the path traversed by an electron per second is numerically equal to its velocity v it follows that the number of ionizing events per unit time is equal to $n_0 v_e \sigma_i$. This quantity is a function of the energy of the electron, since both σ_i and v_e are functions of W. In order to determine the number of ionizing events per second per cubic centimetre of plasma, one must consider all the electrons, whatever their energy. The final result will, of course, depend on the electron temperature T_e for a given electron and neutral-particle concentration. As long as the electron temperature is not too high, and kT_e is small in comparison with the ionization energy, the total number of ionizing events will also be small, so that they can only be due to fast electrons which lie on the tail of the energy distribution, that is, that part of the curve in Fig. 28 which lies well to the right of the maximum. The number of such electrons is very small, and therefore the total rate of ionization in plasma is also quite small. In this temperature range, the rate of ionization is a very rapidly increasing function of T_e. Conversely, at very high temperatures, when kT_e is much greater than the ionization energy of the atoms, the number of ions produced per second in the plasma is a much more slowly varying function of T_e and at very high T_e the ionization rate tends to decrease.

Collisions between electrons and atoms can also give rise to the excitation of the atoms. Under these conditions the electrons transfer to the atom a fraction of their energy, and this lifts the atom from the ground state to one of the possible higher energy states.

It is well known that the energy of an atom cannot vary continuously, but must be equal to one of a series of discrete values, say, W_I, W_{II}, and so on. This can be represented by an energy-level diagram which is illustrated schematically in Fig. 36. The ground state of the atom is represented by the lowest energy level A_I. The impact of an electron may raise the atom to one of the higher energy levels. Transitions of this kind are indicated in the figure by the arrows. The energy lost by the electron, and absorbed by the atom during the transition to its excited state, is equal to the difference between the energies corresponding to the excited and the ground states. For the hydrogen atom, the minimum

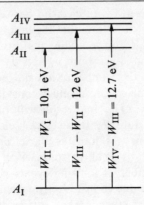

FIGURE 36. *Schematic energy-level diagram for hydrogen.*

energy which is necessary to raise it to the first excited state is 10.15 eV, while for helium and mercury atoms this figure is 20.55 and 4.9 eV, respectively. The minimum excitation energies for other atoms lie between a few electron volts and 15–20 eV. Electrons are also capable of exciting *ions* provided the latter still retain some of their original electrons. Thus, for example, when a sufficiently fast electron collides with a singly charged helium ion, which carries a single electron, the electron may be raised to the first excited state. The minimum energy necessary for this to happen is 40.5 eV.

The effective excitation cross section σ_{ex} is a function of the energy of the incident electron. A characteristic form of this dependence is shown in Fig. 37. As can be seen, after the incident electron has reached the threshold value, equal to $W_{II} - W_I$, the effective cross section increases very rapidly, reaching a maximum at an energy which is not very different from $W_{II} - W_I$. This is followed by a decrease in the cross section. In this part of the curve the energy dependence of σ_{ex} is similar to the corresponding curve for the ionization cross section. The maximum value of the excitation cross section for most neutral atoms is of the order of 10^{-17} to 10^{-16} cm². The excited atom usually retains its extra energy for a very short interval of time (less than 10^{-8} sec). It then returns to the ground state and gives

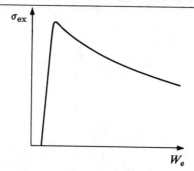

FIGURE 37. *Characteristic form of the dependence of the excitation cross section on the energy of the incident electron.*

up the surplus energy in the form of radiation by emitting a quantum of light, that is, a photon.

It is well known that the photon is a discrete bundle of radiant energy. The energy of a photon is equal to $h\nu$, where h is a universal constant known as Planck's constant and ν is the frequency of the corresponding oscillations. Planck's constant h is equal to 6.6×10^{-27} erg sec.

The frequency of the light emitted by an excited atom when it undergoes a transition from a state of energy W_B to a state of energy W_A is given by

$$h\nu = W_B - W_A. \qquad (3.16)$$

The wavelength of the emitted radiation is given by

$$\lambda = \frac{c}{\nu}. \qquad (3.17)$$

Hence, using (3.16) and (3.17) we find that

$$\lambda = \frac{hc}{W_B - W_A}. \qquad (3.18)$$

In this expression the energy difference $W_B - W_A$, which is converted into radiation, is expressed in ergs. When it is expressed in electron volts, we have

$$\lambda = 1.23 \cdot 10^{-4} \frac{1}{W_B - W_A}, \qquad (3.19)$$

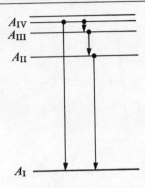

FIGURE 38. *Example of a stepwise transition of an excited atom from the level A_{IV} to the ground state.*

where λ is in centimetres. It follows from this expression that when the emitted energy amounts to 1 eV, the corresponding wavelength is 1.23 μ which lies in the infrared region, adjacent to the visible region. In the case of the hydrogen atom, the first excited state lies 10.15 eV above the ground state, and therefore when the atom returns to the ground state the wavelength of the emitted radiation is 0.12 μ which lies in the far ultraviolet. Under the conditions which are usually realized in the laboratory or in technological installations, the energy of most of the photons emitted by excited plasma atoms is not less than 4–5 eV, and therefore most of the radiation is emitted in the ultraviolet. However, an appreciable portion of the radiation may be emitted in the form of low energy photons. This is due to the fact that an excited atom may return to the ground state by a number of successive transitions rather than by a single transition to the ground state (Fig. 38). The radiation emitted by excited atoms or ions usually plays a leading role in the general energy balance of plasma radiation.

The excited atoms in plasma can also lose their surplus energy by collisions of the second kind. Thus, the excited atom may transfer its surplus energy to one of the plasma electrons which happens to collide with it. The process is, in fact, the exact inverse of the excitation of an atom by electron impact. Collisions of the second kind are usually unimportant in plasma with a low concentration of charged particles, since an excited atom will usually succeed in getting rid of its extra energy by emitting a photon before it undergoes a collision of the second kind. However, in some cases the lifetime of the excited atom may turn out to be relatively long (on the atomic scale), and therefore the probability that a collision of the second kind will take place will be greater. This occurs whenever the excited atom is in a metastable state. For example, a helium atom raised to the energy level which lies at 19.75 eV above the ground state may remain in this level for a time of the order of 10^{-4} sec, since the laws of atomic physics lead to the conclusion that the transition to the ground state with the emission of a photon is not very probable (such transitions are referred to as forbidden). Therefore, a metastable helium atom has a distinct chance of disposing of its surplus energy either by giving it up to one of the free plasma electrons or by colliding with the solid wall of the container. The atoms of other noble gases and many other elements exhibit analogous properties in some of their states.

So far, we have been concerned with collisions in which one of the colliding particles was a free electron. Under certain conditions, collisions between ions and neutral atoms, in which a charge transfer takes place, may be important from the point of view of the properties of plasma. In this process, an ion colliding with an atom receives an electron from it, leaving the atom in an ionized state while itself becoming neutral. This may be described by the following formula

$$A^+ + B \rightarrow A + B^+.$$

Charge-transfer processes have a high probability when the ion A^+ and the atom B belong to the same element, for example, in the case of a collision between a proton and a hydrogen atom, or between a helium ion and a helium atom.

In the case of resonant charge transfer, the effective cross section for the process may be quite high, particularly at low energies when the two particles slowly pass each other. For example, the effective charge-transfer cross section for protons on hydrogen atoms is about 0.5×10^{-14} cm^2 when the energy of the protons is of the order of a few electron volts. It should be noted that this is greater than the geometrical cross section of the hydrogen atom by a factor of the order of 100. Nonresonant charge transfer is characterized by a smaller effective cross section whose maximum value is of the order of 10^{-16} cm^2. Charge transfer processes are important since, under certain conditions, they are an effective mechanism for cooling the plasma ions.

4

Radiation

Hot plasma containing a high concentration of charged particles may act as a very powerful source of radiant energy. The radiation is produced largely as a result of various types of collisions between the plasma particles. Let us consider them in turn.

4.1 Bremsstrahlung

When a free electron passes through the electric field of an ion or atom, there is a change in the direction and magnitude of its velocity. A large instantaneous change in the velocity of a charged particle leads to the appearance of electromagnetic radiation whose energy is supplied at the expense of the kinetic energy of the particle. This means that, during its collision with an atom, an electron may lose a part of its energy by emitting a photon. The energy $h\nu$ of the photon may amount to any fraction of the initial kinetic energy W_e of the electron, but its maximum value is W_e. The appearance of a photon with this maximum energy signifies that all the kinetic energy of a fast electron has been converted into electromagnetic radiation. Since $h\nu$ can also assume any other value between 0 and W_e, the emitted radiation, or the bremsstrahlung as it is commonly called, has a continuous spectrum of frequencies between 0 and W_e/h, in contrast to the radiation emitted by excited atoms which consists of discrete spectral lines of definite wavelengths. Plasma is not the only source of bremsstrahlung. A more common example is the radiation emitted by x-ray tubes, used for diagnostic or therapeutic purposes in medicine. In an x-ray tube a beam of fast

81

electrons, which are emitted by a hot tungsten wire (cathode), is accelerated by a potential difference of some tens of thousands of volts and is allowed to bombard a second electrode, the anticathode or anode. On penetrating into the anode, the fast electrons interact with the electric field of the atoms and emit bremsstrahlung as they come to rest. Owing to the high energy of these electrons, the frequency of the emitted electromagnetic waves is very high and therefore the wavelength is very small (of the order of 10^{-9} to 10^{-8} cm, characteristic of x rays.)

The frequencies of the electromagnetic waves emitted by plasma at an electron temperature T_e lie within very broad limits, but most of the emitted radiation corresponds to photons with frequencies of the order of kT_e/h and wavelengths of the order of ch/kT_e. Therefore, the bremsstrahlung emitted by plasma with $T_e = 10,000°K$ lies mainly in the infrared and in the visible parts of the spectrum, while at $T_e = 10^8°K$ (high-temperature plasma in experimental thermonuclear reactors) most of the radiation lies in the x-ray region. The total intensity of the bremsstrahlung emitted by plasma per unit volume is proportional to the number of electron-ion collisions per second, which in turn is proportional to $n_e n_i$. Moreover, the intensity of the radiation is very dependent on the charge carried by the ions since the probability that a photon will be emitted during an electron-ion collision increases with the electric field which acts on the electron and changes its velocity. Theoretical calculations show that the energy emitted per second per unit volume by a fully ionized plasma at the temperature T_e is given by

$$Q = 1.5 \cdot 10^{-27} n_e\, n_i\, Z^2 \sqrt{T_e}, \tag{4.1}$$

where Q is expressed in ergs per unit volume per second and Z is the atomic number of the element whose ions are the constituents of the plasma. As an example, let us suppose that we have succeeded in producing a hydrogen plasma with electron temperature $T_e = 10^8°K$ and an electron concentration equal to 10^{16} cm^{-3}. According to (4.1), each liter of this plasma will generate about 150 kW in the form of x rays, which is equivalent to the total intensity generated by several thousand simultaneously operating x-ray tubes. The intensity is even higher in the case of heavier ions.

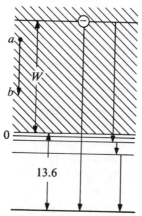

FIGURE 39. *Possible transitions during the recombination of an electron and a proton (schematic).*

4.2 Recombination Radiation

The phenomenon of recombination involves the capture of a free electron by an ion when the electron passes close to it and, therefore, results in a bound state. The energy which is liberated in this process is equal to the sum of the kinetic energy of the free electron and its binding energy. For example, when an electron with energy W_e is captured by a proton to form a hydrogen atom in the ground state, the total energy which becomes available is $W_e + 13.6$ eV (Fig. 39).

The shaded area in the energy diagram corresponds to free electrons. The kinetic energy of such electrons is measured by the vertical distance from the zero line. The ground state of the electron in the hydrogen atom corresponds to a negative energy[10] of 13.6 eV. The available energy can be emitted in the form of a photon with energy $W_e + 13.6$ eV. Another process by which the system may dispose of its energy is that in which the atom first

---

[10]The zero level of energy is conventionally assumed to correspond to the state in which the bond between the proton and the electron is just reduced to zero and the two particles are taken to a very large distance from each other with zero kinetic energy.

undergoes a transition to one of the possible excited states from which it then decays to the ground state. The number of photons which will be emitted under these conditions may be two or more, as shown on the right-hand side of the energy-level diagram in Fig. 39. The emission of bremsstrahlung can also be indicated on this diagram. It corresponds to a change in the energy state of the electron in the shaded region and can be represented by a transition such as $a \rightarrow b$.

Since free electrons have continuous energy spectrum, the photons which are emitted in the recombination process form a continuous spectrum upon which is superimposed the line spectrum of the excited atoms, produced as a result of the stepwise transitions mentioned above. The total intensity of the recombination radiation is, clearly, also proportional to $n_e n_i$. In contrast to bremsstrahlung, the intensity of recombination radiation decreases with increasing electron energy and is therefore enhanced by a reduction in the electron temperature T_e. In hydrogen plasma with $n_i = n_e$, the intensity of recombination radiation per unit volume can be estimated from the expression

$$Q_{\text{recombination}} \approx 10^{-22} \frac{n_e^2}{\sqrt{T_e}}. \tag{4.2}$$

Up to temperatures of the order of $10^7 \,^\circ K$, the intensity of recombination radiation exceeds that of bremsstrahlung. At higher temperatures bremsstrahlung predominates. Moreover, the intensity of recombination radiation increases rapidly with the number of elementary charges carried by the ions. (It is approximately proportional to the fourth power of the ionic charge.)

4.3 Radiation Emitted by Excited Atoms and Ions

The origin of this radiation has already been discussed. In the case of plasma, its intensity is strongly dependent on the electron temperature and the chemical composition, and increases rapidly with the number of heavy ions in the plasma. The spectrum of this radiation consists of discrete lines corresponding to the various transitions between the excited energy states of the atoms and ions.

With increasing electron temperature, there is a gradual increase in the charge on the heavy ions and the line emission spectrum is modified. Thus an atom in a plasma at a very low electron temperature will either remain neutral or will lose one of its most weakly bound electrons. With increasing electron temperature, the inner, more tightly bound electrons will also be removed, and therefore the mean charge per ion will increase. Moreover, this will be associated with an increase in the excitation energy of the ions, with the result that the line spectrum will be displaced from the visible region into the ultraviolet and x-ray regions. The situation may become clearer if we consider some numerical examples. Hydrogen plasma can be practically fully ionized at an electron temperature of 10 eV (100,000°K). If the concentration is 10^{13} cm^{-3}, the total intensity of radiation which is emitted at this temperature is 5×10^{-24} erg per cm^3. Most of this radiation is due to electron-proton recombinations. Suppose now that we add one atom of oxygen to every hundred atoms of hydrogen. The introduction of this small amount of oxygen impurity will increase radiation losses very considerably. In fact, the radiation loss will now be mainly due to the line spectrum of the excited atoms and ions of oxygen, and if the electron temperature is the same (100,000°K), the total intensity emitted by the plasma will be higher by a factor of about 10,000.

The line spectrum emitted by excited atoms and ions in plasma at a not too high electron temperature is one of the main means by which the plasma loses its energy. The energy lost in this way by hydrogen plasma at an electron temperature of the order of 100,000°K with a 10% oxygen impurity is greater by three orders of magnitude than the energy lost by bremsstrahlung from hydrogen plasma with $T_e = 10^8$°K and the same electron concentration.

4.4 Betatron Emission from Plasma

A new source of radiation comes into play when plasma is placed in a magnetic field. The electrons now execute circular motion in the plane perpendicular to the magnetic field, and since the motion is accelerated (the acceleration is directed towards the center of the circle) it should, in accordance with the laws of electrodynamics, give rise to the appearance of radiation. For a single electron the intensity of this radiation is proportional to the square of the magnetic field and is also a function of the velocity of the electron executing the Larmor rotation. The amount of energy radiated by the electron per second is $6.4 \times 10^{-21} H^2 W \sin^2\alpha$, where H is the magnetic field, W is the energy of the electron in electron volts, and α is the angle between its velocity and the direction of the magnetic field. This expression is valid provided the velocity of the electron is small in comparison with the velocity of light, which is practically always the case in plasma. Radiation of this kind is usually referred to as *betatron radiation* and is of major importance in accelerator technology. When electrons are accelerated to high energies in a modern circular accelerator, a stage is eventually reached when the energy spent in accelerating the electrons is used mainly to compensate the betatron radiation losses.

Betatron radiation has a line spectrum in which the fundamental frequency corresponds to the Larmor frequency of the electrons. In addition to the fundamental frequency there are also harmonics, that is, frequencies which are multiples of the fundamental frequency. The relative importance of these harmonics in the total intensity of the radiation increases with increasing W. Betatron radiation lies mainly in the radio frequency range. The wavelength corresponding to the fundamental frequency is [in view of (2.17)] given by

$$\lambda = cT_H = \frac{2\pi m_e c^2}{eH}. \tag{4.3}$$

The wavelengths of the harmonics are $\lambda/2$, $\lambda/3$, and so on. In a magnetic field of the order of 1000 Oe, the radiation consists largely of centimeter waves, while at $H \sim 10,000$ Oe it lies in the millimeter range.

The radiation emitted by plasma is made up of the contributions from the individual electrons. The total intensity of betatron radiation produced per unit volume is therefore proportional to n_e. At high electron concentrations and magnetic fields, a very considerable amount of energy could be lost by betatron radiation if it were

allowed freely to leave the plasma. However, in reality, the long-
wave radiation corresponding to the fundamental frequency and its
lowest harmonics are strongly absorbed by the plasma itself, and
therefore the total flux of radiation escaping through the surface of
the plasma is only a small fraction of the energy generated at internal points. B. A. Trubnikov, working at the Kurchatov Institute of
Atomic Energy, has shown by direct calculation that, at very high
electron temperatures ($10^8 \, ^\circ$K or more), the escape of betatron radiation from plasma increases rapidly because there is an increase in
the fraction of the energy associated with the higher harmonics
which correspond to short wavelengths. Betatron radiation is
therefore a limiting factor in the production of high-temperature
plasmas.

4.5   Flux of Energy Emitted by Plasma

In order to obtain an insight into the nature of the radiation
emitted by plasma, it will be useful to compare plasma with a perfect
blackbody. A perfect blackbody is defined as a body which completely absorbs all radiation falling upon it, whatever the wavelength. Theoretical calculations, which have been confirmed by
experiment, predict that the total intensity of the radiation emitted
by a blackbody is proportional to the fourth power of its absolute
temperature, and that the energy emitted by a blackbody is equal to
$5.7 \times 10^{-5} \, T^4$ erg per cm^2, sec. The spectrum of blackbody radiation is illustrated in Fig. 40, in which the energy emitted per unit
area per unit frequency interval from the surface of a blackbody
is plotted as a function of the frequency of the radiation ν.

The most important features of the blackbody spectrum can be
summarized as follows:

1. At low frequencies, when the photon energies $h\nu$ are much
smaller than kT (the energy which characterizes the thermal energy
of the blackbody particles) the intensity is proportional to ν^3. If
we compare the intensity per unit frequency range at a given frequency in different temperatures, we find that the intensity is proportional to the cube of the temperature.

2. The intensity of blackbody radiation has a maximum at

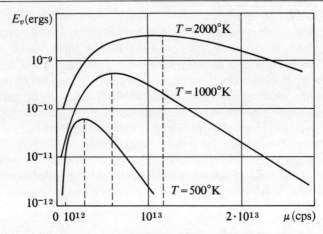

FIGURE 40. *Spectra of blackbody radiation at different temperatures.*

$h\nu \approx 2.75\ kT$. With increasing temperature, this maximum is displaced towards higher frequencies. At temperatures between 7,500° and 15,000°K, the maximum lies in the visible range. At temperatures of the order of some tens of thousands of degrees, the maximum lies in the ultraviolet and corresponds to wavelengths of the order of 0.1 μ. As the temperature is increased still further, the blackbody will eventually become an extremely powerful source of x rays.

In distinction to a blackbody, plasma at a relatively low electron temperature is almost totally transparent to visible and ultraviolet radiation. It will strongly absorb only radiowaves, that is long-wave radiation. In view of the above discussion, this radiation can only be produced in a strong magnetic field. Therefore, if the radio-frequency region of the spectrum is ignored, it may be considered that the total amount of energy emitted by plasma of constant density and temperature is proportional to its volume. Suppose, for example, that this volume is spherical in form. The total energy which is radiated by the plasma is then proportional to a^3, where a is the radius of the ball of plasma, and the intensity of radiation emitted per unit area of its surface is proportional to the ratio of the volume to the surface area; that is, it is a linear function of a.

However, this increase cannot continue indefinitely since, according to the general laws of radiation, the energy which is emitted by the surface of a heated body cannot exceed the energy emitted by the surface of a blackbody. This refers not only to the total amount of energy, but also to the intensity in each individual spectral region. The physical reason which leads to the reduction in the rate of increase of the intensity of the plasma radiation is that, when the volume occupied by the plasma is large, absorption becomes more and more important. Absorption first becomes appreciable in the long-wave region of the spectrum; it is only when a becomes very large that it affects ultraviolet and x-ray radiation. We note, by the way, that at a temperature of $10^8 °K$, which is considered the minimum temperature for future thermonuclear reactors, the radiation emitted per unit area of a blackbody is approximately equal to 5×10^{17} kW. At this rate of emission a sphere of unit volume placed at a distance of one million kilometers from the earth would give rise to a flux of radiation at the earth's surface which would be greater than the flux of solar radiation, although the radiation would consist mainly of x rays. Further calculations show that, in fact, a plasma with a concentration of 10^{16} cm^{-3} and a temperature of $10^8 °K$ will emit an energy flux corresponding to a blackbody at a temperature of only about $2000 °K$. Therefore, a small volume of high-temperature plasma will, in point of fact, be a relatively modest source of radiation.

5

Electric Current, Diffusion, and Thermal Conductivity

5.1 Electric Current in Plasma

Directed motion of electrons and ions in plasma may be due to two causes: an electric field producing a current, or a difference in the concentration between different regions in the plasma. In a nonuniformly heated plasma, the transfer of particles between regions at different temperature gives rise to plasma heat conduction, that is, the flow of thermal energy. Phenomena of this kind are collectively referred to as transfer phenomena. The appearance of an electric current, which we shall consider first, is of particular importance in plasma physics. A current flows because the electric field acting on charged particles of different sign makes them move in opposite directions. In a time t, an electron will acquire the additional velocity $(eE/m_e)t$, while a singly charged ion will receive the additional velocity $(eE/M_i)t$. If there were no collisions between the electrons and the ions, and also between the electrons and ions and the neutral particles, their velocities would increase indefinitely and the plasma would soon be converted into two streams of fast particles travelling in opposite directions. However, in reality, collisions do take place and the particles maintain a directed motion for only a limited time.

The acquired velocities are lost as a result of collisions, after which the particles are again accelerated by the field. We note that the term "collision" is used in the sense defined in Chapter 2.

Usually, the total velocity acquired by an electron or ion in one free path is quite small in comparison with the thermal velocity, and therefore an external electric field has only a slight effect on the motion of the particles. The small extra velocity in the direction of the electric field is superimposed on the fast random motion which takes place at thermal velocities. We can therefore speak of a relatively slow drift of charged particles in the direction of the field, rather than the formation of a current in which the velocities of all the particles have the same direction. A current in plasma is due to the directed motion of charged particles of both signs. However, the contribution due to the positive ions is negligible in comparison with the contribution due to the electrons, since the ions have a much larger mass and therefore smaller acquired velocity. The contribution of the ions to the electric current will therefore be neglected henceforth and we shall confine our attention to the motion of the electrons.

A constant current in plasma consists of a steady stream of electrons in which the force on each particle due to the electric field is balanced by the frictional force due to collisions between the electrons on the one hand and ions and neutral atoms on the other. The frictional force is equal to the momentum (mass multiplied by velocity) which is lost per second by the moving electron to the ions and atoms in the plasma.[11] Let the velocity of the beam of electrons in the plasma be denoted by u, so that the average momentum of electrons is $m_e u$. Since an electron undergoes ν collisions per second, in each of which it loses its velocity and transmits a momentum $m_e u$ to an ion or atom, it follows that the frictional force on an electron is $m_e u \nu$. The condition, that in equilibrium the forces acting on the electron must be equal and opposite, is then

$$m_e u \nu = eE, \qquad (5.1)$$

and hence the average drift velocity is given by

$$u = \frac{eE}{m_e} \cdot \frac{1}{\nu} = \frac{eE}{m_e} \tau, \qquad (5.2)$$

[11]We recall that, in accordance with Newton's second law, force is equal to the rate of change of momentum.

where $\tau = 1/\nu$ is the mean time between successive collisions experienced by electrons. The current passing through a unit area at right-angles to the direction of the electric field in the plasma (Fig. 41) is defined as the current density and is equal to the net electric charge passing through the unit area per second. If the average drift velocity of the charges — in the present case, the electrons — is u, all the charges which lie in a parallelepiped of unit base area and length u will pass through the unit area in one second. If the density of the electrons is n_e, the total number of electrons in the parallelepiped is $n_e u$ and the total charge is $n_e e u$. Therefore, the current density j is given by

$$j = e n_e u = \frac{n_e e^2}{m_e} \tau E. \tag{5.3}$$

This can conveniently be rewritten in the form

$$j = \eta E, \tag{5.4}$$

where η is the conductivity and is given by

$$\eta = \frac{n_e e^2 \tau}{m_e}. \tag{5.5}$$

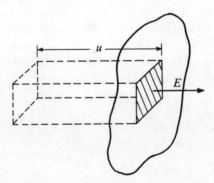

FIGURE 41. *Flux of electrons passing through a unit area per second.*

Equation (5.4) is another way of writing Ohm's law.[12] In Equation
(5.5), τ represents the mean time between collisions which reduce
the velocity of the electron current. Therefore, τ is related to the
quantities τ_{ei} and τ_{e0}, which were defined earlier, by

$$\frac{1}{\tau} = \frac{1}{\tau_{ei}} + \frac{1}{\tau_{e0}}. \tag{5.6}$$

In contrast to Equation (3.7), the latter expression does not include
the term representing electron-electron collisions since these should
not lead to a retardation of the electron current, that is, to a reduction in the drift velocity.

In order to obtain an insight into the properties of plasma as a
conductor of electricity, it will be useful to consider two extreme
cases. The first of these cases corresponds to fully ionized plasma
and the second to plasma with a very small relative concentration of
charged particles. To begin with, consider the first of these two
cases. Since there are no neutral atoms, there are no collisions between electrons and neutral atoms, and therefore $\tau = \tau_{ei}$. Substituting for τ_{ei} from (3.14) into (5.5), and remembering that in a fully
ionized plasma $n_e = n_i Z$ where Z is the charge of the ions, we have[13]

$$\eta = 0.9 \cdot 10^7 \frac{T_e^{3/2}}{Z}. \tag{5.7}$$

Equation (5.7) has certain important consequences. First, it shows
that the conductivity of fully ionized plasma is independent of the
concentration of electrons. This is understandable because as n_e increases, there are more particles acting as current carriers and more
collisions; that is, there is a reduction in the mean free time.

[12]For readers who are accustomed to the more general way of writing Ohm's
law, namely, $I = U/R$, where I is the current, U the potential difference, and R
the resistance, we must point out that Equation (5.4) is equivalent to this expression. In point of fact, $I = jS$, where S is the cross section of the conductor,
$U = El$ where l is the length of the conductor, and $R = \kappa l/S$, where κ is the
resistivity. Substituting these expressions into the formula relating I, U, and R,
we find that $j = E/\kappa$, where $1/\kappa$ is by definition the electrical conductivity of the
plasma. We thus arrive again at Equation (5.4).
[13]This expression is given in cgs units. In order to convert it into practical
units, the electrical conductivity should be divided by 9×10^{11}.

Second, for a given electron temperature, the conductivity is inversely proportional to the mean charge per ion. Finally, the conductivity of a fully ionized plasma is proportional to $T_e^{3/2}$ and will therefore become very great at high temperatures. For example, the conductivity of hydrogen plasma at different temperatures is given in the following table:

T_e (°K)	η (cgs)
10^4	10^{13}
10^5	$3 \cdot 10^{14}$
10^6	10^{16}
10^7	$3 \cdot 10^{17}$
10^8	10^{19}

At an electron temperature of about 15×10^6, hydrogen plasma has the same electrical conductivity as ordinary metallic copper at room temperature.

Under certain conditions, an interesting phenomenon, known as *electron runaway*, occurs in fully ionized plasma. We have assumed that an electron is accelerated in a time τ and its drift velocity is lost on collision with an ion. This means that the electron component of the plasma moves as a whole with a constant velocity. However, a simple argument will show that all the electrons cannot have the same mean velocity. Thus consider an individual electron whose velocity is much greater than the mean thermal velocity of the electron component. An electron of this kind corresponds to the tail end of the energy distribution and its mean free time is much greater than the mean value τ. Moreover it has been shown (see Equation (3.10)) that the effective scattering cross section is inversely proportional to the fourth power of the velocity, and therefore the mean free path is directly proportional to v^4 and the mean free time is proportional to v^3. It follows that, in the interval between successive collisions, our particular fast electron is accelerated by the field to an additional velocity which is much greater than the mean drift velocity u. For example, if the kinetic energy of the electron is higher than the mean thermal energy by a factor of

10, the drift velocity to which it is accelerated in the electric field is found to be higher than the mean drift velocity by a factor of 30. Thus, if the initial velocity of the electron is high enough, the mean free path may be so large that the additional velocity acquired exceeds the thermal velocity. However, this means that we can no longer use the simple model in which the electron loses its extra velocity as a result of collisions, since this model is only valid when the extra velocity is small in comparison with the thermal velocity. Moreover, we should recall the discussion of the physical meaning of quantities such as the mean free path and the mean free time between collisions in plasma, which was given in Chapter 2 where it was noted that these quantities cannot be easily fitted into a simple scheme involving gas-kinetic concepts only.

The extreme case we have just considered is an illustration of a situation in which the simple gas-kinetic model must be abandoned in favor of the true physical description. In point of fact, acceleration and deceleration of an electron occur continuously rather than discretely. While the electron is receiving its additional velocity, collisions with ions gradually alter its direction of motion. If the initial velocity of the electron is very high, its interaction with the ions will be considerably reduced, and therefore the increase in the drift velocity produced by the electric field will not be compensated by a collisional loss of the longitudinal velocity component. This means that the accelerating and frictional forces will no longer be in equilibrium and the electron will be continuously accelerated by the electric field. This process will occur in the case of those electrons in the Maxwell tail which succeed in reaching in one free path an additional velocity greater than the initial velocity v. Mathematically, this condition may be written in the following form:

$$\frac{eE}{m_e}\tau > v. \tag{5.8}$$

It has already been pointed out that τ is proportional to v^3 and inversely proportional to the ion concentration, so that $\tau = (\alpha/n_i)v^3$, where α is a numerical coefficient. Substituting this expression into (5.8), we see that the continuous acceleration of the electron begins when Ev^2/n_i exceeds a certain maximum value. As the electric field increases and the concentration of the plasma decreases, the magnitude of the initial velocity v which is necessary to satisfy (5.8) decreases, and therefore there is a corresponding increase in the fraction of the electron component of the plasma which is continuously accelerated. This means that in addition to the current which obeys Ohm's law, there will also be a current of accelerated electrons whose velocity, and therefore energy, will increase with time.

When E/n_i is high enough, the condition given by (5.8) will be satisfied not only for electrons in the tail of the Maxwell distribution but also for those with velocities of the order of the mean thermal velocity. Most of the plasma electrons will then be continuously accelerated and the usual ohmic current will be absent altogether. Theoretical calculations show that electron runaway becomes appreciable when the ratio of the mean drift velocity of the plasma as a whole to the mean thermal velocity of the electrons is greater than about 0.1. The ratio of the drift velocity to the thermal velocity is proportional to the kinetic energy of the electrons since this ratio involves the factor v^2. Therefore, if $u/v = 0.1$ for electrons with the mean energy, then for electrons with kinetic energy of the order of $10\ kT_e$, the ratio of u to v will be of the order of unity and such electrons will take part in the runaway process.

The necessary condition for continuous acceleration of electrons is that the plasma conductor must be long enough; that is, the electrons must have a long distance available for the acceleration process. This condition can easily be satisfied in a toroidal chamber in which the electrons are accelerated by an electric field induced, for example, with the aid of the transformer arrangement illustrated in Fig. 42. Continuous acceleration of a relatively small number of electrons can, in fact, be observed experimentally. Energies of the order of a few million electron-volts can be achieved in a field of only a few tens of volts per orbit.

Theoretical analysis of the behavior of a beam of continuously accelerated electrons in plasma leads to the conclusion that, under certain conditions, such currents are capable of exciting various plasma oscillations and waves which take over the energy acquired by the electrons during their acceleration in the electric field.

Processes of this kind may give rise to an additional deceleration of charged particles, so that the acceleration process will terminate when the electrons reach a certain energy.

Consider now the passage of an electric current through an ionized gas with a very low degree of ionization, that is, the case where the deceleration of the electrons is due mainly to collisions with netural atoms and molecules in the gas. Under these conditions $\tau = 1/n_0 v \sigma_a$, where n_0 is the concentration of neutral particles and σ_a is the effective collision cross section between electrons and neutral particles. It has already been pointed out in Section 3.2 that σ_a is, in general, a relatively complicated function of electron energy. In cgs units, the conductivity of a weakly ionized gas is given by

$$\eta = \frac{n_e}{n_0} \cdot \frac{e^2}{m_e} \cdot \frac{1}{\overline{v_e \sigma_a}}, \tag{5.9}$$

where the bar over the product $v_e \sigma_a$ represents the mean of this quantity (with allowance for the electron-velocity distribution and the dependence of σ_a on v_e). In very approximate calculations, we may assume that v_e is equal to the mean thermal velocity of the

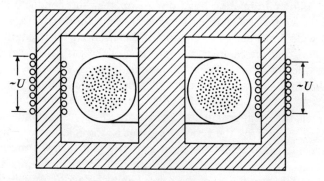

FIGURE 42. *Toroidal discharge chamber surrounding the core of a transformer.*

electrons and σ_a can be taken at this velocity. The product of these two parameters should not then be very different from the true mean of the product $v_e \sigma_a$.

Equation (5.9) shows that the conductivity of a weakly ionized plasma is proportional to the relative ionization n_e/n_0. Since this ratio enters as a factor into (5.9), the conductivity of a weakly ionized plasma should be small (simply because of the very small number of current carriers). Low-density plasma is encountered in low-current electric discharges, where the temperature of the electrons depends on the ratio of the electric field E to the gas pressure p_0. This may be written in the following symbolic form $T_e = f(E/p_0)$. This dependence of T_a on the discharge parameters has a simple qualitative explanation. The thermal energy of an electron is determined by the difference between the work done by the electric field and the energy losses due to collisions between electrons and atoms. It is clear that the higher the field strength, the higher will be the energy which an electron can acquire between successive collisions. On the other hand, with increasing pressure there is an increase in the energy losses due to collisions, and therefore the temperature of the electrons should decrease with increasing pressure p_0. Hence, T_e should increase with increasing E and decrease with increasing p_0. The quantity $\overline{v_e \sigma_a}$ is, of course, also a function of E/p_0.

It follows from the above discussion that the conductivity of plasma with a low-charged particle concentration may vary over very wide limits and is a function of the electric field strength, the pressure, and the chemical composition of the gas. It is therefore quite difficult to find a simple relationship which could be used to predict the conductivity of a weakly ionized plasma in each specific case. All that one can do is to note some general points which may be useful in very approximate calculations. First, one would expect that for given E/p_0, the ratio n_e/n_0, that is, the relative ionization, should increase rapidly when an impurity with a low ionization potential is added to the gas. The vapor of an alkali metal is suitable for this purpose. On the other hand, the addition of halides (chlorine or fluorine) should reduce the conductivity very considerably at low E/p_0, since chlorine and fluorine have high electron affinities and can easily capture free electrons. The negative ions produced as a result of this capture have large mass and therefore small mobility in the electric field. The conductivity of plasma with a low relative ionization cannot, in general, be high. A high conductivity η at a low E/p_0 can only be achieved if the effective collision cross section is small, but this requires a high electron temperature which is inconsistent with the assumed low relative ionization. The practical limit for the electrical conductivity of a weakly ionized gas is of the order of 10^{12} cgs. This means that the resistivity of a weakly ionized gas will be higher than the resistivity of copper by a factor of at least a few tens of thousands. Continuous acceleration of electrons is, in principle, also possible at very low pressures and very high electric field-strengths in neutral or weakly ionized gases. However, in this case, the initial conditions necessary for this phenomenon to occur are much more rigid than for fully ionized plasma, since the electrons must now be accelerated through the energy range in which the collision cross section has a maximum.

5.2 Plasma in a High-frequency Field

Suppose now that a high-frequency alternating current flows through the plasma. We shall assume that the frequency of the electric field, which gives rise to this current, is so high that a large number of oscillations take place during the time corresponding to a mean free path. The effect of the collisions on the behavior of the electrons is then very small, and can be neglected; that is, it may be supposed that the only forces acting on the electrons are those due to the high-frequency field. In order to determine the current due to the alternating field, we can use the results of Section 2.4, which are represented graphically in Fig. 7. One of the more important conclusions of that analysis is that the phase of the velocity lags behind the phase of the field by 90°. Since the electric current is proportional to the electron velocity in the direction of the current, it must also lag behind the field. Therefore, the phenomenon is analogous to that encountered in *AC* theory when one considers the properties of an inductance, for example, an ordinary coil.

However, the origin of the phase lag is quite different in the two cases. The alternating current flowing through a coil gives rise to an alternating magnetic field; this induces an additional electromotive force in the wire which must be compensated by the external voltage applied to the coil. It is the induced field which is responsible for the phase difference between the voltage and the current. In the case of a high-frequency current in plasma, the phase difference between I and U is not associated with a magnetic field. It is simply due to the fact that the current carriers, that is, the electrons, have a finite mass and oscillate as mass points in the periodically varying field of force. The density j of the high-frequency current at any given time is $n_e e u$, where u is the velocity of the electrons in the direction of the field and is given by (2.8). Therefore, the expression for the current density flowing through plasma is

$$j = \frac{n_e e^2}{m_e \omega} E_0 \sin \omega t, \qquad (5.10)$$

where ω is the angular frequency of the electric field. All the quantities in this expression are in cgs units. The amplitude j_0 of the current, that is, its maximum value, is related to the amplitude of the electric field E_0 by $j_0 = n_e e^2 E_0 / m_e \omega$. Equation (5.10) is valid when the time between collisions is large in comparison with the period of the high-frequency oscillations. When this conditions is not satisfied, the plasma exhibits not only a kind of inertial inductance but also a finite resistivity.

The lower part of Fig. 7 shows the variation in the position of an electron under the influence of a high-frequency field. Just as in the case of mass point executing oscillations under the influence of a periodic force, the displacement of the electron under the action of the alternating electric field lags in phase behind the velocity by 90°. Hence, the displacement S lags 180° behind the force; that is, the displacement is in a direction opposite to the direction of the force. It follows that the high-frequency properties of plasma are the reverse of those of ordinary dielectrics.

In order to obtain a better understanding of these special properties of plasma, consider the situation illustrated in Figs. 43a and b. These figures represent the displacement of charges in an ordinary dielectric and in plasma. For convenience, it is assumed that in both cases only the electrons are displaced. Inspection of the left-hand drawing, which represents an ordinary dielectric, shows that the electrons move in the direction of the forces acting upon them,

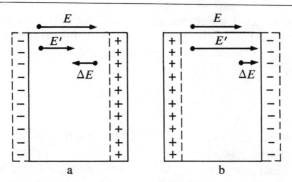

FIGURE 43. *Displacement of charges in an electric field:*
a. ordinary dielectric, b. plasma.

that is, in the direction opposite to the direction of E. The displacement of the electrons results in the appearance of charges on the surface of the dielectric. The electrons appear on one surface and the positive ions on the other. (In the absence of the field, the positive charges neutralize the electrons.) The surface charges produce a field ΔE whose direction is opposite to that of the external field; that is, the resultant field in the dielectric, E', is less than the applied field. The ratio of the external field to the reduced field inside the dielectric is known as the dielectric constant or permittivity and is usually denoted by ϵ. In general, the permittivity ϵ is a function of the frequency of the electric field and is always greater than unity. For some substances, for example, barium titanate, the value of ϵ at moderate frequencies is greater than 10^4.

Consider now Fig. 43b, which illustrates what happens in plasma. The electrons are now displaced in the direction of the field, and thus the charges appearing on the surface tend to increase the field strength inside the plasma. Therefore, the permittivity of plasma is less than unity. The lower the frequency of the oscillations, ω, the larger the amplitude of the electron oscillations. Therefore, with increasing ω, the permittivity of plasma decreases; detailed calculations show that ϵ is zero when

$$\omega_k = \sqrt{\frac{4\pi n_e e^2}{m_e}}, \qquad (5.11)$$

which is the "critical frequency." We shall encounter it again later. It turns out that the angular frequency of the natural electron oscillations in the plasma is equal to ω_k and the permittivity ϵ is given by

$$\epsilon = 1 - \frac{\omega_k^2}{\omega^2}. \tag{5.12}$$

It is evident that when $\omega < \omega_k$, the permittivity is negative.

This effect is related to an important property of plasma. About one hundred years ago, Maxwell showed that the relation between the permittivity ϵ and the refractive index γ for electromagnetic waves in matter is

$$\gamma = \sqrt{\epsilon}, \tag{5.13}$$

which shows that a negative ϵ leads to an imaginary refractive index and therefore an imaginary velocity of propagation of electromagnetic waves in matter (since this velocity is proportional to the ratio of the velocity of light in vacuum to the refractive index). In other words, when ϵ is negative, electromagnetic waves cannot propagate through matter and are reflected from it. Therefore, at frequencies smaller than the critical frequency, plasma is a perfect reflector of electromagnetic waves. This is the reason why radio waves can be sent around the Earth. It is known that a layer of rarefied plasma, called the ionosphere, is located between 40 and 200 km above the Earth's surface. Reflection of radio waves from the ionosphere is responsible for the long-range propagation of radio waves, that is, propagation to points lying beyond the visible horizon. The minimum wavelength λ_k of radio waves which can pass through plasma is given by

$$\lambda_k = \frac{c}{\gamma_k} = \frac{2\pi c}{\omega_k}. \tag{5.14}$$

Substituting for the critical frequency ω_k from (5.11), we have

$$\lambda_k = c\sqrt{\frac{\pi m_e}{n e_e^2}} = \frac{3.3 \cdot 10^6}{\sqrt{n_e}}. \tag{5.15}$$

When $\lambda < \lambda_k$, the refractive index of plasma can be obtained from

$$\gamma = \sqrt{1 - \frac{\lambda^2}{\lambda_k^2}}. \tag{5.16}$$

which is a consequence of (5.12), (5.13), and (5.14).

5.3 Motion under the Action of a Pressure Difference

Directed currents of electrons and ions can be produced in plasma, not only by an electric field but also by a gradient in the concentration of the particles. Consider the behavior of a nonuniform plasma with a high degree of ionization. Figure 44 depicts a region occupied by a nonuniform plasma whose concentration decreases from left to right, in the direction of increasing x. We shall assume for simplicity that the electron temperature T_e is equal to the ion temperature T_i throughout the region. A change in the concentration will then be proportional to the change in the pressure of the plasma since $p = nk(T_e + T_i)$. The decrease in the

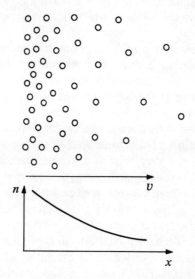

FIGURE 44. *Schematic representation of a gas with a nonuniform distribution of concentration along the x axis.*

concentration in the direction of the x axis means that there is a corresponding decrease in the pressure.

Plasma, just as an ordinary gas, cannot exist in equilibrium in the presence of a pressure gradient and will redistribute itself until there are no pressure differences. In the present example, the plasma will move from left to right. This process is analogous to the expansion of a gas in an apparatus in which, by opening a valve, we release the gas from a high pressure region into a low pressure region.

The simplest example of this is the expansion of a gas into a vacuum. This expansion occurs with a velocity of the order of the mean thermal velocity of the molecules. A similar situation should obtain in a stream of expanding plasma. However, plasma consists of two components and the problem arises as to which of the two thermal velocities — the electron or the ion velocity — should play the leading role in the expansion process. This question can easily be answered. Since the plasma as a whole is quasi-neutral, the electrons cannot leave the slowly moving ions far behind, and therefore the plasma as a whole will expand with the thermal velocity of the ions.

There are, however, some exceptions to this general rule. If a concentration of plasma with a nonuniform pressure distribution is formed in a very short interval of time in a region bordering on a high vacuum, then at the initial instant of time a relatively small number of electrons will leave the surface of the plasma with thermal velocities. The electric field which is produced as a result will, under certain and still somewhat obscure conditions, lead to the appearance of a very brief and weak stream of very fast ions moving with velocities approaching the thermal velocity of the electrons. A very large number of electrons is necessary to produce a single fast ion, since the velocity of the ion is taken at the expense of the velocity of the electrons. This situation is occasionally observed in electric discharges of short duration in a low-density gas. However, it may be regarded as an exception which does not invalidate the general rule governing the motion of expanding plasma as a whole.

So far, we have only been concerned with the limiting case of nonuniform plasma with a very large relative variation of pressure. Small pressure changes are much more frequently encountered. The time necessary for the pressures and concentrations to become equal is then much longer. In the general case, analysis of this situation can be based on the basic laws of mechanics.

A pressure difference gives rise to a force which accelerates the gas in accordance with the second law of Newton. Let us try to determine the effect of this force by first estimating its magnitude. Consider a unit cube in a gas, which is oriented so that one of its edges is parallel to the direction of the pressure drop. The force acting on a side surface of the unit cube is numerically equal to the pressure (since pressure is equal to the force acting per unit surface area). On the left, the pressure is equal to p_0, and on the right it is equal to p_1, which is smaller than p_0. It follows that the force acting on the unit cube is equal to $p_0 - p_1$. This pressure difference will, in fact, accelerate the gas in the unit cube. Since the mass of the gas in the unit cube is equal to its density ρ, it follows that the acceleration is equal to $(p_0 - p_1)/\rho$. This is, of course, only a very approximate calculation, since the acceleration will vary from point to point within the cube, owing to the differences in the density and the relative pressure difference.

Let us therefore replace the unit cube by a very small cube of side ξ. The area of a side surface of this cube is then ξ^2, its volume is ξ^3, and the mass of the enclosed gas is $\rho\xi^3$. The resultant force giving rise to the motion of the gas is $(p_0 - p_1)\xi^2$, where p_0 is the pressure on the left and p_1 the pressure on the right. The acceleration is given by

$$a = \frac{p_0 - p_1}{\xi} \cdot \frac{1}{\rho}. \tag{5.17}$$

The quantity $(p_0 - p_1)/\xi$ is the pressure drop per unit length. However, this is not a simple quantity, since it is characterized both by a magnitude and a direction. In point of fact, it is a special type of vector. When preceded by a minus sign, it is called the pressure gradient, which in vector analysis is represented by the symbol grad p. The negative sign is necessary to allow for the fact that the direction of the gradient is in the direction of increasing pressure, whereas the force acting on the gas is in the direction of decreasing p. The concept of the gradient will be frequently encountered in the following chapters, because in the physics of plasma we are always concerned with the gradients of pressure, concentration, and temperature. It will therefore be useful to discuss this in somewhat greater detail.

In the above simple case there was no doubt as to the direction of the pressure gradient, since it was assumed that the pressure varied along the x axis only; that is, it was a function of a single co-ordinate only. In general, the pressure inside the plasma may vary in all directions and the form of the variation will not, in general, be very simple. Suppose, for example, that the plasma is in the form of a cylinder, not necessarily of circular cross section. A cylinder of this kind can be produced in an electric discharge in a long glass or ceramic tube. When the cylinder of plasma is long enough, the pressure in its middle region will be nearly constant in the longitudinal direction, but will decrease in the transverse direction. The pressure distribution over a typical cross section of the cylinder might be of the form shown in Fig. 45. The closed lines in this figure represent lines of equal pressure. In physical geography they are known as isobars. The larger the number of

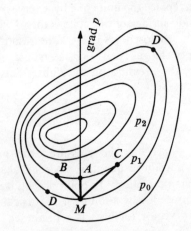

FIGURE 45. *Definition of gradient. The direction of the gradient is indicated by an arrow.*

isobars which are drawn on a particular map, the more accurately they represent the distribution of pressure in the plasma. The point M lies on an isobar on which the pressure is, say, p_1. The pressure varies in all directions except for the direction parallel to the isobar (the line DD in Fig. 45). However, the form of the variation in p is different along different lines drawn through M. The next isobar, which represents the somewhat higher pressure p_2, can be reached in various ways, for example, along MA, MB, or MC. In all such cases the total change in the pressure is equal to $p_2 - p_1$, although it occurs over different lengths. The maximum rate of change in the pressure occurs in the direction of MA, which corresponds to the shortest distance between the two isobars. The ray MA is approximately perpendicular to both isobars. The direction of the most rapid change in the pressure is, in fact, the direction of the pressure gradient which is numerically equal to $(p_2 - p_1)/MA$, provided that the neighboring isobars do not differ in pressure by too much, that is, provided that the network of isobars is sufficiently dense. This definition of the gradient may be generalized to the case in which the pressure varies not only in a plane, but in all directions in space. In this most general situation we must consider *surfaces* of constant pressure, and the gradient is in the direction of the shortest distance between two neighboring surfaces of constant pressure, that is to the perpendicular between them (Fig. 46). This

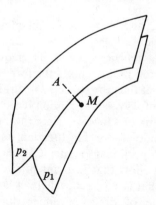

FIGURE 46. *Surfaces of constant pressure. The line MA is parallel to the direction of the gradient.*

analysis of the concept of the gradient is quite general. It can be used to define gradients in the concentration, temperature, electric potential, and so on. The gradient of any quantity varying in space is measured by the increase in that quantity per unit length in the direction of its most rapid variation.

Under certain conditions, a nonuniform distribution of charged particles in plasma may give rise to another kind of motion which is known as *diffusion*. In a completely ionized plasma, the diffusion process may be isolated from dynamic processes due to pressure differences, only if the plasma contains a number of different kinds of ions with different spatial distributions. However, a much more interesting case is the phenomenon of diffusion of charged particles in weakly ionized plasma when the pressure due to the electron and ion components is small in comparison with the pressure of the neutral gas.

Diffusion is similar to the flow of a current in that it involves the mixing of the components of the medium rather than the displacement of the medium as a whole. A typical example of diffusion in everyday life is the spread of the scent due to a drop of aromatic substance in a room, or the gradual disappearance of a puff of cigarette smoke. A clear picture of the diffusion process can be obtained by observing the behavior of a microscopic particle in a liquid under a microscope. (This is the Brownian motion; see Fig. 29.)

Diffusion in a gas, and in particular in plasma, is the result of the random motion of the particles (atoms, ions, or electrons). As a result of collisions, a particle frequently changes its direction of motion, and its path takes the form of a tortuous zigzag line. If at an initial time the particle is at the point 0 (see Fig. 29), then as a result of its random motion it will depart from this point in the course of time. However, since the motion of the particle takes place in a randomly varying direction, its distance from the point 0 will not be proportional to time. Calculations based on the theory of probability show that in point of fact the distance r is proportional to $\sqrt{t}$, that is $r = \sqrt{At}$, where A is a constant which characterizes the rate of diffusion under different conditions.

Consider now the macroscopic effect of such random motions in

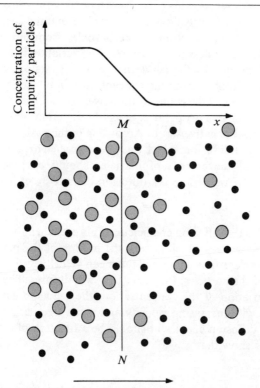

FIGURE 47. *Schematic representation of a nonuniform distribution of impurity particles (large circles) in the volume occupied by a gas (small circles).*

the case of a gas containing a small amount of impurity, which is distributed nonuniformly as shown in Fig. 47. On the left of the plane MN the concentration of the impurity particles is greater than on the right. Therefore, during their random motion, more particles will travel from left to right than in the reverse direction. This means that there is a net flux of impurity particles in the positive direction of the x axis. The intensity of this current across the plane MN is equal to the difference between the number of particles passing per second per unit area in the direction of the arrow, and the number of particles passing through unit area per second in the opposite direction. It is clear that the larger the difference in the concentration of the particles from left to right, the larger the magnitude of the current. The variation in the concentration is indicated by the curve in Fig. 47. The slope of this curve gives the rate of drop in the concentration n of the impurity. The relative change in the concentration over a small part of the x axis is a measure of this drop. It is precisely the concentration gradient (taken with a negative sign). According to the basic assumptions of the theory of diffusion, which have been verified experimentally, the intensity of the current of particles should be proportional to $-\operatorname{grad} n$. If we denote the diffusion current by Q, we have

$$Q = -D \operatorname{grad} n, \tag{5.18}$$

where D is the diffusion coefficient. This coefficient is related to the various quantities which govern the motion of the particles in the gas. It is clear that the larger the mean velocity and the mean free path λ of the particles, the faster they will diffuse. Therefore, for a given variation of the concentration, the diffusion current should increase with increasing velocity and mean free path. This means that the diffusion coefficient should be a function of v and λ. Calculations show that

$$D = \frac{1}{3}v\lambda. \tag{5.19}$$

For readers who are interested not only in the theoretical results expressed by Equations (5.18) and (5.19), but also in the way in which these formulas may be obtained, we give a derivation based on the simplest ideas (whose main disadvantage is its somewhat formal nature). This derivation is unimportant to our subsequent discussion and may be omitted altogether by readers who are not interested in mathematical proofs.

A change in the concentration of particles in space means that there is also a change in the pressure of the component of the gas to which these particles belong. If the temperature is assumed to be the same at all points, then Equation (3.1), which relates p, n, and T, shows that the pressure gradient is simply proportional to the concentration gradient, and their ratio is equal to kT. However, as has already been pointed out, the quantity $-\text{grad } p$ is simply the force acting on all the particles enclosed in a unit volume. The force acting on a single particle is therefore given by

$$F = -\frac{kT}{n}\text{grad } n. \tag{5.20}$$

In diffusive motion this force is balanced by the frictional force due to collisions between impurity particles and atoms in the main mass of the gas. The latter force is proportional to the mean velocity of directed motion u of the impurity atoms. To determine u we can use an argument analogous to that employed in Section 5.1 to calculate the current in a plasma. The frictional force is equal to the momentum which is transferred per unit time by a moving particle to the atoms in the main component of the gas. The total loss of momentum per second is equal to $mu\nu$, where m is the mass of the particle and ν is the number of collisions per second. In equilibrium this quantity must be equal to F, and therefore

$$mu\nu = -\frac{kT}{n}\text{grad } n. \tag{5.21}$$

Hence

$$nu = -\frac{kT}{m\nu}\text{grad } n. \tag{5.22}$$

The quantity on the left-hand side of this equation is the diffusion current Q. We have thus proved Equation (5.18). The coefficient in front of the concentration gradient is none other but the diffusion coefficient D, and therefore

$$D = \frac{kT}{m\nu} = \frac{kT\lambda}{m\upsilon}. \tag{5.23}$$

The mean kinetic energy of the particles is related to the temperature by Equation (1.2), which we shall now write in the form

$$\overline{W} = \frac{m}{2}\overline{v}^2 = \frac{3}{2}kT.$$

Substituting the expression for kT into Equation (5.23), we arrive at Equation (5.19).

The above derivation (which does not pretend to be rigorous) is particularly instructive in one respect. It shows that diffusion is a process which is in some ways similar to the electric current. It is due to a force which brings the particles into motion. This force is the pressure difference. Owing to the presence of the gaseous phase in which diffusion takes place, the pressure difference is balanced by a frictional force. Moreover, there is a clear distinction between diffusion and all processes involving the motion of a gas as a whole, which occur whenever there is an uncompensated pressure gradient in the main component.

So far, we have been concerned with diffusion in a neutral gas. Let us now consider how it can take place in plasma. It should be clear from the foregoing discussion that if we are dealing with fully ionized plasma, we cannot speak of diffusion in the presence of a concentration gradient because the plasma is then set in motion as a whole. When the degree of ionization is small, the situation is quite different. The electrons and ions then form an impurity component whose density and pressure are small in comparison with the corresponding quantities for the main neutral component of the partially ionized gas. If there are irregularities in the distribution of the charged particles, they will diffuse through the neutral component. A characteristic feature of this process is that, since the plasma is quasi-neutral, the rate of diffusion should be the same for both electrons and ions. Since the electrons have a greater mobility, they leave the ions behind giving rise to an electric field which decelerates them very rapidly while slightly accelerating the heavy ions. As a result, the velocities tend to become equal, and the diffusion process occurs at a rate which is nearly the same as the rate of diffusion of the ions in the absence of the electric field. The diffusion coefficient for plasma can be determined from (5.19) by substituting into it the values of v and λ calculated for ions. The process which involves the simultaneous motion of ions and electrons through the gas is known as ambipolar diffusion.

The thermal conductivity of plasma is also due to the motion of particles. The main role in the transport of heat from the hotter parts of plasma to the cooler parts is played by the electrons (because of the higher thermal velocity which they have). If there is a temperature drop in a given direction, electrons with higher energies will travel toward one side, while electrons with lower energies will travel in the opposite direction. As a result, there is a net flow of thermal energy toward the colder layers of plasma. This flow is proportional to the relative temperature drop, that is, the temperature gradient. In fact, the expression for the flow of heat through unit area is

$$Q_T = -C_T \text{ grad } T,\qquad (5.24)$$

where C_T is the thermal conductivity. The higher the temperature of the plasma (we are assuming for the sake of simplicity that the temperature is the same for both electrons and ions), the higher the thermal conductivity. The magnitude of C_T in fully ionized plasma, containing singly charged ions only, can be estimated from the following very approximate formula

$$C_T = 1.24 \times 10^{-6} \, T^{5/2} \text{ erg per cm deg.}\qquad (5.25)$$

The thermal conductivity given by this formula is expressed in c.g.s. units. If the heat flow is expressed in calories, then the thermal conductivity is given in calories per degree per centimeter. This will necessitate the replacement of the numerical factor in (5.25) by the new factor 3×10^{-14} cal per deg. It follows from Equation (5.25) that the thermal conductivity of a fully ionized plasma increases very rapidly with temperature. At $T \sim 10^5 °K$, the thermal conductivity of hydrogen plasma is higher than the thermal conductivity of silver at room temperature.

6

Experimental Techniques

In order not to give the impression that the physics of plasma is a purely theoretical subject, consisting solely of formulas and abstract ideas, we must give, even if only briefly, an outline of the more important experimental methods which are used to investigate the properties of plasma. The main practical problem is to determine the basic parameters which characterize the state of plasma, that is to say, the concentration of charged particles, the mean kinetic energy, the energy distribution of electrons, and the mean energy of the ions. Moreover, it may be necessary to measure the plasma drift velocity, the flow of energy to the walls, the current of accelerated electrons, and so on. A very large number of different experimental techniques is available for these purposes. The most valuable information has been obtained from (a) Langmuir probes, (b) investigations of the passage of radio waves through plasma, and (c) spectroscopic studies of plasma. These three methods are considered in turn in the following sections.

6.1 The Probe Method

The probe method, which was first introduced by Langmuir about forty years ago, can be used to determine the electron concentration, temperature, and energy spectrum, and to estimate the ion temperature. In this method, a measurement is made of the current to a small metal electrode (probe) when different voltages are applied to the probe. This yields a curve called the probe characteristic of plasma. Figure 48 illustrates schematically the

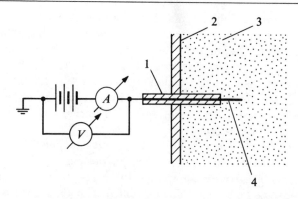

FIGURE 48. *The Langmuir probe: 1 — insulating tube, 2 — wall of discharge chamber, 3 — plasma, 4 — probe.*

experimental arrangement, whilst Fig. 49 shows a typical probe characteristic (in somewhat idealized form). The probe may be in the form of a plane disk, cylinder, or sphere. The wire which is used to conduct the current from the probe is surrounded by an insulating cover. It is important to ensure that the dimensions of the probe are small, since otherwise the presence of the probe affects the state of the plasma.

Consider now a probe characteristic in which the voltage applied to the probe is plotted along the x axis, and the current flowing

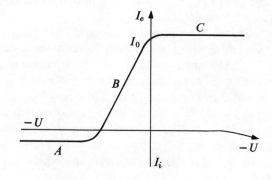

FIGURE 49. *Tpyical probe characteristic.*

into the probe from the plasma along the y axis. Positive values of the current represent an electron current; negative values represent an ion current. On gradually increasing the voltage applied to the probe, we successively pass through three different parts of the probe characteristic. In the region marked A in Fig. 49, the current flowing to the probe is due to positive ions. In region B there is a rapid increase in the electron current which reaches saturation (constant value) in the region C.

This form of the curve can be quite simply explained. When the voltage applied to the probe relative to the plasma is large and negative, the electrons cannot reach the probe and the current is due to positive ions only. The current due to these ions is relatively small since, for equal concentrations of electrons and ions, the latter have a much smaller velocity, whilst the magnitude of the current is proportional to the product of the concentration of the particles and their velocity. The electron current is cut off so long as the negative potential on the probe is high enough to prevent the fastest electrons, in the tail of the Maxwellian distribution, from reaching the probe. In order to reach the probe, the electrons must ascend the retarding potential difference and lose kinetic energy by doing work against the electric field.

Suppose that the absolute magnitude of the retarding potential difference is U, which means that the potential of the probe relative to the plasma is $-U$. Only those electrons can reach the probe whose kinetic energy is greater than eU. Since the kinetic energy of the electrons is of the order of kT_e, it follows that the electron current to the probe will remain cut off as long as kT_e is much less than eU. A current will appear when kT_e and eU are of the same order of magnitude. Calculations show that if the electron energy distribution follows Maxwell's law, then the fraction of the total electron current which reaches a probe at a potential U is e^{-eU/kT_e}. Therefore, when $eU = kT_e$, only 37% of the electron current will reach the probe. When $eU = 2kT_e$ this figure becomes 12%, and when $eU = 3kT_e$, only 4% of the electrons reach the probe. Thus the general expression for the probe current in this region of the characteristic is

$$I = I_i + I_0 e^{-eU/kT_e}, \tag{6.1}$$

where e is the base of the natural logarithms ($e = 2.718$), I_0 is the electron current in the absence of a retarding field, and I_i is the ion component of the current. The latter component is opposite in sign to the electron current, but its magnitude is very small in comparison with the electron current. The ion current I_i may be determined from the part of the characteristic which lies in region A, and we may assume that it remains practically the same in region B. By subtracting the ion current, we obtain the electron component for any retarding potential U. The potential U must, of course, be measured from the point on the x axis at which the knee of the curve begins, that is from the point at which the electron current ceases to increase, having reached its limiting value.

In practice, it is convenient to interpret probe measurements by plotting the logarithm of the electron current as a function of the probe potential U. In view of Equation (6.1) this graph (Fig. 50) represents the equation

$$\ln I_e = \ln I_0 - \frac{e U}{k T_e}. \qquad (6.2)$$

The slope of the graph is e/kT_e from which the absolute electron temperature T_e can be calculated. We note that this method of determining T_e is based on the assumption that the electron energy distribution is Maxwellian, so that the electron current is proportional to e^{-eU/kT_e}. The probe characteristic itself may serve as a

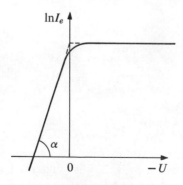

FIGURE 50. *Probe characteristic on a semilogarithmic scale.*

confirmation of the fact that the distribution is Maxwellian. This is best shown by the logarithmic graph which we have just mentioned. The dependence of the logarithm of the electron current on U will be linear, provided Maxwell's law is valid. Experiment shows that this is practically always the case, and therefore the above method for the determination of T_e can be used in most cases.

Knowing T_e and the total electron current I_0, we can determine the concentration of electrons in plasma. In order to simplify our discussion, let us suppose that the probe is in the form of a flat disk. The electron current per square centimeter of surface of the probe is proportional to $n_e \bar{v}_e$, where $\bar{v}_e$ is the mean thermal velocity of the electrons in the plasma. If the velocity of each of the plasma electrons were perpendicular to the plane of the probe, and all the electrons were moving towards the probe, then the magnitude of the current which we have just mentioned would not be merely proportional, but actually equal to $n_e \bar{v}_e$. In reality, only one half of the electrons move towards the probe, and the other half move in the opposite direction. This reduces the current by a factor of 2. Moreover, it is important to take into account the fact that the velocity of the electrons is not necessarily perpendicular to the plane of the probe. Calculations show that when this effect is taken into account the current is reduced by an additional factor of 2. Therefore, the final expression for the maximum electron current to a probe of area S is given by

$$I_0 = \frac{e n_e \bar{v}_e S}{4}. \qquad (6.3)$$

This formula may be used to determine the electron concentration in plasma from probe measurements. In principle, it is possible to determine both the electron and the ion temperature from the probe characteristic. However, the ion temperature is usually much smaller than the electron temperature and is exceptionally difficult to determine, since there are many factors which mask the effect of the ion temperature on the form of the probe characteristic.

Probe characteristics provide unambiguous information about properties of plasma only under certain special conditions. For example, when the density of the plasma is high, so that the mean free paths of the electrons and ions are very small, the above simple method of measuring T_e and n_e cannot be used. The interpretation of probe measurements is also very difficult, or even quite impossible, when a strong magnetic field is present in the plasma. However, in spite of these limitations, the probe method is in practice one of the most widely used methods because of its relative simplicity.

6.2 Radio-wave Measurements

The electron concentration can be measured, or at least estimated by studying the transmission of radio waves through plasma. According to Equation (5.15), the maximum wavelength of radio waves which will pass through plasma with electron concentration n_e is $3.3 \times 10^6/\sqrt{n_e}$. Therefore, when $n_e = 10^6$ particles per cm³, the critical wavelength is equal to 33 m, while when $n_e = 10^{12}$ particles per cm³ the limiting wavelength is reduced to 3.3 cm. The basic arrangement for this kind of experiment is illustrated schematically in Fig. 51.

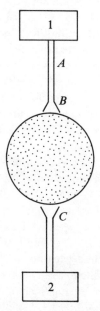

FIGURE 51. *Basic arrangement for measuring the absorption of electromagnetic waves in plasma: 1 — high-frequency oscillator, 2 — receiver.*

Radio waves from a high-frequency oscillator are transmitted through a hollow metal waveguide A leaving it through the horn B in the form of a collimated beam. This beam is then allowed to pass through the chamber containing the plasma and is received by another horn C. The wavelength λ is determined by the properties of the oscillator and cannot be varied within wide limits in a given measuring channel. If the receiver records that the radiation has passed through the chamber, this means that the wavelength λ is smaller than the critical value. This immediately provides a value for the upper limit of the electron concentration. Thus, if the plasma transmits the radiation we have $n_e < 1.1 \times 10^{13}/\lambda^2$, while if it does not, then $n_e > 1.1 \times 10^{13}/\lambda^2$.

These upper and lower limits are not, of course, sufficient. More complete information may be obtained by using two or more wavelengths at the same time. Suppose, for example, that a beam containing waves with $\lambda = 4$ mm and $\lambda = 8$ mm is employed, and it is found that the 4 mm waves are cut off. This means that n_e must lie between 2×10^{13} and 8×10^{13}. In order to determine the electron concentration rather than find its upper and lower limits, it is necessary to modify the experimental method. For example, the determination of n_e may be based on the fact that the refractive index of plasma is a function of the electron concentration, and therefore the velocity of propagation of electromagnetic waves in plasma is also a function of n_e. Let us suppose that electromagnetic oscillations of frequency ν pass through a layer of plasma of thickness d. The number of wavelengths which may be fitted into a segment of length d is d/λ, where λ is the wavelength in the plasma. Since $\lambda = u/\nu$, where u is the velocity of propagation of the waves in the plasma, and $u = c/\gamma$ where γ is the refractive index, we find that the number of wavelengths which can be fitted into the segment of length d is equal to $\nu\gamma d/c$. This may be rewritten in the form $\gamma d/\lambda_0$ where λ_0 is the wavelength of waves of the same frequency but propagating in a vacuum.

Figure 52 illustrates schematically an apparatus which may be used to determine γ by measuring the number of wavelengths which can be fitted into a layer of plasma. The high-frequency oscillator emits electromagnetic waves which pass along a metal waveguide.

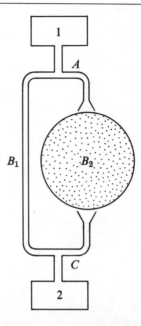

FIGURE 52. *Basic arrangement for measuring the refractive index of plasma by measuring the number of wavelengths which can be fitted into a layer of plasma: 1 — high-frequency oscillator, 2 — receiver.*

At the point A the radiation is divided into two parts, one of which travels via B_1 along the bent continuous waveguide, while the other travels along B_2 and passes through a chamber containing the plasma. The two waves are reunited at C. The intensity of the radiation recorded by the receiver depends on the result of the recombination at C. If the two waves reach the point C in phase, that is if the crests of one coincide with the crests of the other, as in Fig. 53a, then the two waves interfere constructively and the signal recorded by the receiver reaches a maximum value. If, on the other hand, the waves differ in phase by 180° and the crests of one of the waves correspond to the troughs of the other, then there is destructive interference, and the strength of the signal is reduced (Fig. 53b). Suppose that, to begin with, there is no plasma in the container.

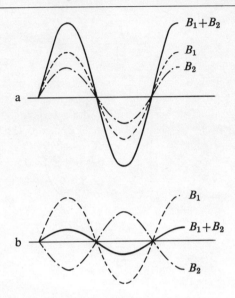

FIGURE 53. *Graphs illustrating the interference of signals propagating along the two channels B_1 and B_2 in Fig. 52:* a. *maximum resultant amplitude,* b. *minimum resultant amplitude.*

The geometry of the waveguides can be adjusted so that the waves reaching C have zero phase difference, and therefore add constructively. If the chamber is now filled with plasma whose concentration is gradually increased, the phase difference between the waves reaching C will gradually increase, since the number of wavelengths occupying the region filled by plasma will vary. If the concentration of plasma is small, the refractive index γ will be very nearly equal to unity, and the number of wavelengths fitting into the plasma layer will differ from the corresponding number in the absence of the plasma by a small fraction of one oscillation. This means that the crests of the waves at C will be separated by a very small amount. As n_e is increased, the phase difference will increase and the amplitude of the resultant wave reaching the detector will decrease. For a certain value of n_e the phase difference will be 180° and the signal recorded by the receiver will be a minimum. Further increase of n_e will lead to the eventual coincidence of the crests, which is associated with a new maximum in the strength of the signal, and so on.

All this is shown graphically in Fig. 53. It follows that the amplitude of the received signal is a periodic function of n_e. By measuring the strength of the signal with gradually increasing plasma density, it is possible to determine the refractive index γ at any particular density and then, by using Equations (5.15) and (5.16), it is possible to find the concentration. This is called the radiointerferometer method, since it is based on the interference between two waves. A necessary condition for the successful operation of the interferometer is that the frequency of the radio waves should be greater than the critical frequency for the particular state of the plasma. In addition, the thickness of the layer of plasma, through which the radio waves are transmitted, must be known.

6.3 Plasma Spectrometry

One of the more important sources of information about the properties of plasma are studies of the spectral composition of the radiation emitted by plasma. Such studies may be carried out with various spectographs, that is, normal prism instruments with glass or quartz optics, which are suitable for the analysis of the visible and near ultraviolet radiation, or vacuum spectographs with diffraction gratings, which are suitable for short wave radiation (far ultraviolet or even x rays). The radiation enters the slit of the spectrograph, either through a window in the vessel containing the plasma or through a connecting evacuated pipe (if one is interested in radiation which does not pass through glass or quartz). The intensity of the spectral lines emitted by plasma depends on the concentration of electrons and ions, and on the electron temperature. With increasing electron temperature, the spectrum changes: New lines, corresponding to a higher degree of excitation of the atoms, appear. At high electron concentrations, lines due to excited neutral atoms have an appreciable intensity only if the electron temperature is low enough, and disappear very rapidly as this temperature increases (owing to ionization of the neutral component). They are replaced by lines due to singly- or multiply-charged ions.

A very approximate estimate of the electron temperature can be obtained by measuring the relative intensity of the spectral lines emitted by a given atom or ion. For example, let us suppose that an excitation energy W_I must be communicated to an atom or ion before it can emit a particular spectral line, while the energy necessary for the appearance of another line is $W_{II} > W_I$. The intensity of each of these lines will depend on the number of electrons which have an energy sufficient to produce the excitation process. If the excitation energy is much greater than kT_e, the relative number of such electrons, and therefore the intensity of the line, will be largely determined by the factor e^{-W/kT_e}. Therefore, the ratio of intensities of the two lines is primarily governed by the ratio

$$\frac{e^{-W_I/kT_e}}{e^{-W_{II}/kT_e}} = e^{W_{II}-W_I/kT_e}. \qquad (6.4)$$

This does not mean that the ratio of intensities will be precisely equal to this quantity, since the intensity is also a function of the internal properties of the atom, which have an effect on the transition probability. However, these additional factors are temperature-independent and can be approximately taken into account. Therefore, when $W_{II} - W_I$ is much greater than kT_e, the factor $e^{(W_I-W_{II})/kT_e}$ is very sensitive to the ratio of the line intensities, and its magnitude may be used to estimate the electron temperature.

In some cases, it is possible to use other spectroscopic measurements to determine T_e. For example, if the plasma has a very high concentration, then in the far infrared region it emits as a perfect blackbody at the temperature T_e. Therefore, by measuring the absolute flux of radiant energy emitted by plasma in the form of infrared radiation, it is possible to estimate the electron temperature.

Spectroscopic determinations of plasma concentration are very difficult because they involve the accurate measurement of the absolute intensities of spectral lines. The temperature of the atoms and ions in plasma is usually deduced from various indirect data. However, in some cases, spectroscopic measurements can also be used for this purpose. The point is that the temperature of the atoms is related to the width of the spectral lines emitted by them. This is due to the *Doppler effect*, which relates the frequency of a wave to the velocity of the source. A simple example of the Doppler effect is the increase in the pitch of the whistle from an approaching locomotive, and the reduction in this pitch which is observed as soon as the locomotive moves away. These phenomena are encountered both in acoustics and in optics. For example, if a source of light moves towards the receiver with a velocity u, the frequency of the oscillations measured by the receiver is given by

$$\nu = \nu_0 \left(1 + \frac{u}{c} \right),$$

where ν_0 is the frequency emitted by a stationary source, u is the velocity of the source, and c the velocity of light. The wavelength is related to frequency, and must therefore also depend on u. As the source of light approaches the recording instrument (spectrograph), the wavelength will decrease, and vice versa. In plasma, the atoms and ions move at random with a mean velocity proportional to $\sqrt{T}$. Therefore, different particles emit slightly different wavelengths, with the result that a narrow spectral line is broadened (Fig. 54). Measurements of the width of spectral lines may be used to determine the temperature of the particles which are responsible for the emission of the radiation.

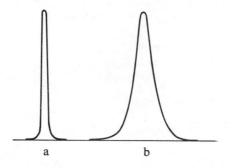

FIGURE 54. *Doppler broadening of a spectral line:* a. *line profile at low ion temperature,* b. *broadening of the line from plasma with a high ion temperature.*

7

Plasma in a Magnetic Field

7.1 Forces Acting on Plasma in a Magnetic Field

The properties of plasma are radically altered when it is placed in a strong magnetic field. The reason for this is that the motion of the charged plasma particles is affected by the magnetic field. In a strong magnetic field, the electrons and ions cannot move freely in the direction perpendicular to the lines of force. The trajectory of each particle takes the form of a helix with axis parallel to the magnetic field, and the motion is therefore highly anisotropic (directed). Figure 55 illustrates the situation for a fully ionized plasma both in the absence and in the presence of a magnetic field.

The displacement of electrons and ions across lines of force is

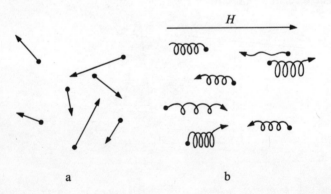

FIGURE 55. *Schematic illustration of the motion of particles in fully ionized plasma:* a. *in the absence of a magnetic field,* b. *in a strong magnetic field.*

only possible as a result of collisions between the particles. In each such collision, the particles are displaced only through a distance of the order of the Larmor radius. In a fully ionized plasma of given concentration, the probability of a collision decreases rapidly with increasing temperature since the average interval of time between collisions is proportional to the cube of the mean velocity, that is, to $T^{3/2}$. Therefore, although at high plasma temperatures a charged particle, having a larger Larmor radius, is displaced through a larger distance after each collision than at low temperatures, the mean distance which it succeeds in traversing per second in the direction perpendicular to the field is, nevertheless, found to decrease with increasing temperature because of the rapid decrease in the collision probability. This distance will also decrease with increasing field strength.

Because a magnetic field restricts the motion of charged particles, it may be used to prevent the plasma from coming into contact with the walls of the container (Fig. 56). In Figure 56, the fully ionized high-temperature plasma occupies a cylindrical volume inside a tube whose axis is parallel to the direction of the external magnetic field. In the space between the surface of the plasma and the walls of the tube there is only vacuum and magnetic lines of force.

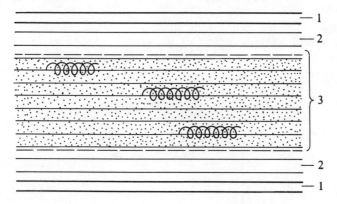

FIGURE 56. *Insulation of the walls of a discharge chamber from plasma by means of a magnetic field: 1 — walls of the chamber, 2 — vacuum, 3 — plasma.*

The situation illustrated in Fig. 56 is not surprising and can easily be explained by considering the motion of electrons and ions in the magnetic field. However, there are considerable difficulties if one tries to interpret the phenomenon from the macroscopic point of view. Plasma retained by a magnetic field exhibits an internal pressure. In the absence of the magnetic field, this pressure would immediately lead to the expansion of the cylinder of plasma, which would thus come into contact with the walls. The problem now arises as to what is the force which balances this pressure.

It is clear that this force must, in some way, be related to the magnetic field. It may be calculated as follows. A force due to a magnetic field can only arise when an electric current flows. For example, consider a conductor carrying a current at right-angles to the magnetic field (Fig. 57). According to Ampere's law, the force acting on the conductor is IH/c per unit length, where I is the current in electrostatic units, H is the magnetic field, and c is the velocity of light. This force acts at right-angles both to the lines of force and to the current. Its direction is indicated by the arrow and is given by the right-hand rule. If the current is distributed continuously through the medium, we can determine the force per unit volume. Thus consider a unit cube in a medium through which a current flows and suppose that the cube is oriented so that the current is perpendicular to one of its faces. The magnitude of the current flowing through the unit area is equal to the current density j in the medium. Suppose that the magnetic field is perpendicular to the current. The unit cube may be looked upon as a conductor of

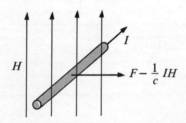

FIGURE 57. *Interaction of a current-carrying conductor with an external magnetic field.*

unit length which carries a current j. The force acting on this conductor must be equal to jH/c.

This conclusion can be generalized somewhat by considering the case when j and H are at an angle different from 90°. Under these conditions, the field strength may be resolved into two components, one of which is parallel $(H_{\parallel})$ and the other perpendicular $(H_{\perp})$ to the current. The component $H_{\parallel}$ has no effect whatsoever on the current and therefore the force is equal to $jH_{\perp}/c$. It can also be written in the form $jH \sin \theta/c$, where θ is the angle between the directions of j and H. In the language of vector algebra, with which we are already familiar, this means that the force acting on the unit cube may be written in the form $\mathbf{j} \times \mathbf{H}/c$.

This is the force which balances the pressure in the plasma when it is placed in a magnetic field. For equilibrium, it is necessary that the electrodynamic force be equal and opposite to the forces acting on the boundary layer due to the pressure drop across it. It has already been explained in Chapter 3 that this force is equal to $-\mathrm{grad}\ p$, and therefore the condition for equilibrium of plasma in a magnetic field is

$$\frac{1}{c}\mathbf{j} \times \mathbf{H} = \mathrm{grad}\ p. \qquad (7.1)$$

This formula is quite general. It holds both for the boundary layer and for any volume element within the plasma.

In order to elucidate the physical significance of Equation (7.1), we must first establish the reason for the appearance of a current. This can be done with the aid of Fig. 58a, which shows the cross section of a cylinder of plasma. The trajectory of each particle in this cross section may be represented by a Larmor circle. For the sake of clarity, only the electron Larmor orbits are shown. Let us suppose that the pressure is constant over the cross section except for a very narrow boundary layer where it suddenly drops to zero. Under these conditions, the Larmor circles are uniformly distributed over the area occupied by the plasma. The motion of the particles inside the plasma does not result in a net current flow since any given point is traversed with equal probability by particles with opposite directions of motion. However, near the boundary,

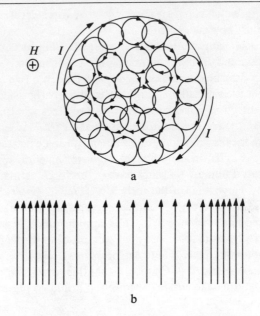

FIGURE 58. a. *Cross section through a column of plasma placed in a longitudinal magnetic field*, b. *the distribution of magnetic lines of force over the cross section.*

the circular Larmor motion leads to the appearance of a current which flows in the form of a thin ring. This current is due to the fact that while at internal points the various Larmor currents cancel out, at the surface they add up. The interaction of the macroscopic surface current with the magnetic field is the reason for the appearance of electrodynamic forces which prevent the plasma from expanding.

One further important consequence of Equation (7.1) must be noted. The force $\mathbf{j} \times \mathbf{H}/c$ is perpendicular to the directions of both the current and the magnetic field. Therefore, grad p is also perpendicular to j and H. This means that the pressure of the plasma is constant along the lines of force. It should also be constant along the lines of current.

The behavior of plasma in a magnetic field can also be described in a different way by recalling that, as a result of the Larmor rotation of the electrons and ions, the plasma as a whole exhibits diamagnetic properties, so that the field inside the plasma is smaller than the field outside, The conventional concept of magnetic pressure, first introduced by Faraday, may be used in this connection. The pressure due to the field is equal to $H^2/8\pi$ and its direction is perpendicular to the lines of force which in Faraday's theory are regarded as if they were elastic filaments stretched in the direction of the field and compressed at right-angles to it. In the case illustrated in Fig. 58b, all the lines of force are parallel, but their density, that is, the number of lines per unit area, which is a measure of the field strength, undergoes a change at the surface. The density is higher outside the region occupied by the plasma. Therefore, the magnetic pressure acts in the inward direction and the difference between the magnetic pressures, that is, the difference between $H_1^2/8\pi$ and $H_2^2/8\pi$, must be equal and opposite to the intrinsic pressure of the plasma which we are assuming to be constant throughout the cylinder. Hence,

$$p = \frac{H_1^2}{8\pi} - \frac{H_2^2}{8\pi}. \tag{7.2}$$

In particular, if the diamagnetic Larmor currents reduce the magnetic field strength inside the plasma to zero, then

$$p = \frac{H_1^2}{8\pi}. \tag{7.3}$$

The higher the concentration and temperature of the plasma, the greater the field strength required to balance the pressure.

The above three ways of describing the behavior of plasma in a magnetic field are equivalent, since they describe the same physical phenomenon in different ways. In particular, Equation (7.1) may be applied to the current flowing in the boundary layer of the plasma, and this will again yield Equation (7.2). Without repro-ducing this proof, we note that, qualitatively, the equivalence of the two methods of determining the electrodynamic forces is a consequence of the relationship between the current density j and the change in H. If the current flows at right-angles to the uniform

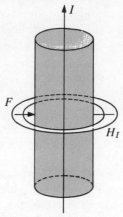

FIGURE 59. *Origin of the forces which compress a cylinder of plasma when a current flows through it (H_1 — magnetic field due to the current).*

magnetic field H, it gives rise to a field whose direction is the same as that of H. Therefore, the field strength varies from point to point, giving rise to a field gradient and therefore a difference in the magnetic pressures.

The above formulas, which relate the pressure of the plasma and the electrodynamic forces, are only valid if the plasma is in equilibrium. It is possible, however, to imagine a situation when there is no equilibrium. As an example, consider a cylinder of cold, low-pressure plasma along the axis of which a rapidly increasing current is allowed to flow. This current gives rise to a magnetic field whose lines of force surround the plasma as indicated in Fig. 59. Interaction of the current with its own magnetic field tends to compress the plasma in the radial direction. This effect may be discussed in terms of the well-known elementary rule which states that parallel currents attract; therefore, any current-carrying conductor tends to contract in the radial direction. If the pressure in the plasma is low, the force tending to compress it is not completely balanced and the plasma will contract at an increasing rate. We shall not discuss this particular case in detail (it will be dealt with later) but will merely note that such nonequilibrium situations are very frequent. They may be described by replacing Equation (7.1) by the more general equation

$$\rho a = \frac{1}{c} \mathbf{j} \times \mathbf{H} - \text{grad } p, \qquad (7.4)$$

where ρ is the density, that is, mass per unit volume, and a is the acceleration of the plasma. All the quantities entering into this equation are given per unit volume. Therefore, the left-hand side consists of the density ρ multiplied by the acceleration, while the right-hand side consists of the vector sum of forces acting on a unit volume of the plasma.

Inspection of Equations (7.1) and (7.4) will show an important property: These equations have nothing in them to indicate that they refer to plasma, since the microscopic structure of the medium enters into them under the guise of the macroscopic parameters ρ, a, and p. The equations can equally well be used for the analysis of phenomena occurring in a strong magnetic field in any conducting medium capable of changing its form under the action of external forces. This means, in particular, that Equations (7.1) and (7.4) are valid not only for plasma but also for a conducting liquid, provided its conductivity is high enough and gravitational and capillary forces can be neglected. Therefore, Equation (7.4) is usually referred to as the basic equation of magnetohydrodynamics.

In our analysis of the behavior of plasma in a magnetic field, we saw that Equation (7.1) could be derived on the basis of macroscopic considerations without explicitly taking into account the laws governing the motion of the ions and electrons, and without discussing the mechanism responsible for the appearance of the electric field in plasma. As long as we are using the conducting liquid model to describe the various processes occurring in plasma, we may consider that the current can flow freely both along and at right-angles to the lines of force. However, we cannot confine our attention to this simplified theory because sooner or later we shall encounter the following question: What effect has the magnetic field on the current flowing through the plasma, and in particular, under what conditions will the current flow at right-angles to the magnetic field? The importance of this question will become apparent if we recall that electrons and ions cannot, in fact, move freely at right-angles to magnetic lines of force.

7.2 Current in a Magnetized Plasma

To begin with, let us consider the simple case when the electric and magnetic fields are parallel. A given electron is then accelerated along the magnetic lines of force, and therefore the magnetic field has no effect on the final velocity communicated to the electron. Since collisions between charged particles occur when they approach each other at very small distances, it follows that the electric forces acting during the collisions are much stronger than the interaction of the charged particles with the magnetic field. (We are concerned here with magnetic fields of the order of a few thousand oersteds, which can easily be produced in the laboratory.) Therefore, when E is parallel to H, the magnetic field should have very little effect on the flow of current.

Let us suppose now that an electric field E is introduced into a uniform plasma in which there is a uniform magnetic field H perpendicular to E. When the electric field is switched on, the electrons and ions begin to move in cycloidal or trochoidal orbits in the direction parallel to the vector $\mathbf{E} \times \mathbf{H}$. At the initial instant of time, this will give rise to the appearance of a current since the electrons and ions will be displaced through a certain distance along the electric field (see Fig. 60 where it is assumed for the sake of sim-

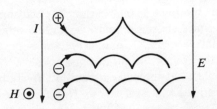

FIGURE 60. *Motion of particles in perpendicular electric and magnetic fields. At the initial instant of time all the particles move so that a current is produced in the direction of the electric field.*

plicity that the trajectories are cycloidal). However, this current will disappear as soon as the cyloidal motion settles down and the entire plasma moves at right-angles to both E and H with the drift velocity cE/H. Since the relative drift velocity of the electrons and ions is zero, there will be no momentum transfer from the electrons to the ions.

If in addition to the electrons and ions there is also a neutral component, the charged particles will undergo collisions with the neutral atoms and molecules, and this will tend to retard the drift of the charged particles. This frictional force will have the same direction but, in general, different magnitude for the electrons and ions. It was pointed out in Chapter 2 that any force which is perpendicular to the magnetic field gives rise to a drift. Therefore, the frictional forces acting on the electrons and ions as they move through the neutral component will also give rise to drift. The velocity of the drift motion due to frictional forces will differ both in magnitude and direction for the electron and ion components, and this will give rise to an electric current in the plasma. A detailed analysis shows that this current will have a component in the direction of E and a further component parallel to $\mathbf{E} \times \mathbf{H}$. It follows that the resultant current will be at an angle both to the electric and magnetic fields. Its magnitude decreases with increasing H and E and with decreasing frequency of collision between the charged particles and the neutral atoms.

This situation persists if the neutral component of the plasma remains at rest as a whole. This is possible under certain conditions. However, if the concentration of the charged particles in the plasma is high enough and the volume of the plasma is large enough for it to be considered practically infinite, then soon after the electric field is switched on, the neutral component is brought into motion with the drift velocity cE/H as a result of collisions with electrons and ions. The relative velocity of the charged and neutral particles is then zero and there is no transfer of drift momentum. Therefore, the retarding force and the current due to it are also zero.

The volume of the plasma need not be infinite in all directions in order to ensure that there is no electric current. It is only necessary that the drift motion with velocity cE/H should take place

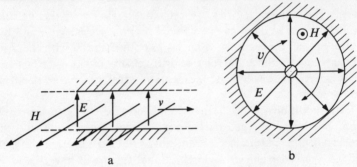

FIGURE 61. *Motion of plasma in perpendicular electric and magnetic fields:*
a. *in the electric field of a plane parallel capacitor,*
b. *in a cyclindrical capacitor.*

freely. This will occur, for example, when a layer of plasma is placed inside a plane-parallel condenser of infinite length (Fig. 61a). A similar situation obtains in the case of plasma rotating inside a cylindrical condenser (Fig. 61b). The current which flows immediately after the electric field is switched on gives rise to charges on the surface of the plasma, just as in an ordinary dielectric. The dielectric properties of plasma in a magnetic field will be discussed later. For the moment, let us assume that there is only an initial pulse of current which rapidly drops to zero. However, a situation of this kind, where the drift motion occurs freely in crossed fields, is the exception rather than the rule. In practice, it is much more probable that, having begun its motion with velocity cE/H, the plasma will come to rest after a short interval of time, either because it encounters a wall or as a result of the appearance of a large pressure drop which prevents any further motion.

Any drift motion perpendicular to the magnetic field in plasma is always due to a force which is perpendicular both to H and to the direction of the drift itself. (The cycloidal motion of charged particles in crossed fields is a special case of this general rule.) Therefore, if the drift velocity is zero, this must mean that the force which is the immediate cause of this drift is balanced by some other force. It follows that in the case under consideration, the drift due to the electric field E will terminate only if the force on each particle due to this field is balanced by an equal and opposite force. In a fully ionized plasma, this can only be the force of friction between the electrons and ions. (In the case of free drift of particles of either sign with the same velocity cE/H, this frictional force is zero.) The compensation of forces leads to the reappearance of normal plasma conductivity in the direction of the electric field, since the conductivity is expressed by the equation $eE = mu\nu$, where u is the velocity of an electron in the direction of the electric field.

Although it is perfectly correct, this discussion may nevertheless appear to be unsatisfactory to the critical reader. Thus termination of drift in the direction of $\mathbf{E} \times \mathbf{H}$ leads to the reappearance of drift in the direction of E. Since this motion is also perpendicular to the magnetic field, there should be a force perpendicular to E which gives rise to drift of the electrons and ions in opposite directions. This force is, in fact, the true cause of the electric current. The problem now is: How can we derive this force?

In order to answer this question, we must start with the fact that the required force should be directly connected with the physical processes which appear as a result of drift in the direction of $\mathbf{E} \times \mathbf{H}$ and which tend to prevent this drift. One such process is the appearance of a variation of concentration and pressure in the plasma. It is precisely this pressure variation which, in the presence of a transverse magnetic field, will give rise to a force tending to maintain the current even though the direction of the current and the direction of the pressure gradient are at 90° to each other.

From the formal point of view, the situation is quite clear. The force equal to $-\operatorname{grad} p$ gives rise to electron and ion drift across the lines of force and at right-angles to the direction of the force. The ions and electrons move in opposite directions, that is, an electric current is produced. If $\operatorname{grad} p$ is perpendicular to E, the current will be parallel to the direction of the electric field. However, this purely formal argument must be amplified by a discussion of the microscopic situation. It is useful to be able to have a picture of how a nonuniform pressure distribution gives rise to the appearance of currents of charged particles.

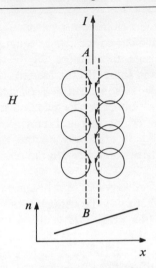

FIGURE 62. *Appearance of a current in a nonuniform plasma in a magnetic field. Only the electron trajectories are shown.*

In the special case when the pressure drop is localized in the boundary layer, the mechanism responsible for the appearance of the current has already been discussed above. A more general case is illustrated in Fig. 62 where it is assumed, for the sake of simplicity, that all the electrons have the same velocities, and therefore the trajectories can be represented by circles of equal radius. The concentration of particles increases from left to right. Consider a narrow band which is parallel to the vertical axis (in the figure it is defined by the two dashed lines). Electrons whose orbits lie to the right of the band AB move in a downward direction inside the band, while those on the left of the band move in an upward direction. Since it is assumed that the electron concentration increases from left to right, it follows that the number of electrons moving in the downward direction within the band must be greater than the number of electrons moving in the opposite direction. There is, therefore, a net current flowing within the band. We thus arrive at an almost paradoxical situation: Each of the electrons moves in a circular orbit without undergoing a net displacement, but there is nevertheless a constant electron current in the direction perpendicular to the concentration gradient, that is, perpendicular to the pressure gradient.

The above discussion may be summarized as follows: If an electric field E is set up in some way in plasma at right-angles to a magnetic field H, the plasma as a whole will move with velocity $\mathbf{E} \times \mathbf{H}$. If there is nothing to retard this motion, the electric current will flow for a very short time only. If, on the other hand, an equilibrium is set up in which the drift motion reaches a steady state, the current is reestablished, and its density is given by the usual formula $j = \eta E$. The real reason for the reappearance of the current in this case is a pressure gradient in the electron component, which is produced as a result of the drift motion.

The following remarks will complete our discussion of currents in plasma:

1. It is clear that an electron pressure gradient may be present when the plasma reaches its equilibrium state. The current-carriers are the electrons, and therefore the electrodynamic forces due to the interaction between the current and the magnetic field act on the electrons. The fate of the ions can be discussed separately. Since the plasma as a whole is quasi-neutral, it follows that the change in concentration of the electrons should lead to a similar change in the concentration of the ions. The problem then arises as to what is the force which produces and maintains the ion pressure gradient. It is evident that this force is due to the electric field which appears as a result of the fact that electrons moving under the action of electrodynamic forces tend to leave the ions behind. In equilibrium, the ion pressure gradient is compensated by the forces on the ions, which are due to the forward-moving electrons. This is expressed by

$$eE' = \frac{1}{n} \operatorname{grad} p_i, \qquad (7.5)$$

where E' is the electric field due to the initial separation of the electrons and ions. The factor $1/n$ on the right-hand side of Equation (7.5) is introduced because we are dealing with the force on a single ion rather than all the ions in a unit volume. Therefore, when one is concerned with the validity of Ohm's law in the case of plasma in a magnetic field, one must remember that the relation between the current and the electric field strength in the plasma does not include the component of the electric field which is balanced by the ion pressure gradient. This means that the field E' in Equation (5.4) need not be taken into account.

2. When the plasma as a whole moves with velocity v, the relation between the current and the field is

$$j = \eta \left(E + \frac{1}{c} \mathbf{v} \times \mathbf{H} \right).$$ (7.6)

This equation shows that, during its motion across the magnetic field, the plasma experiences an induced field represented by the second term in the brackets.[14] This field must always be added to the electric field produced by external sources. It follows from Equation (7.6) that, in the case of plasma moving with a drift velocity cE/H, the quantity in brackets must be equal to zero. This gives a new and independent interpretation of the disappearance of the current in plasma moving freely in crossed fields. The current in a drifting plasma is equal to zero simply because the resultant electric field is zero.

3. Although the relation between j and E in the presence of a transverse magnetic field in plasma in equilibrium is the same as in the absence of the field, this does not mean that the physical picture is identical in the two cases. In particular, it is obvious that, in the presence of a strong transverse magnetic field, the electrons cannot be continuously accelerated.

7.3 Diffusion in a Magnetic Field

The diffusion process, which is due to a nonuniform distribution of the concentration of plasma particles, is completely altered in the presence of a transverse magnetic field. Thus, in the absence of a magnetic field the collisions between particles tend to retard the process causing their concentrations to become equal. In contrast, if a strong magnetic field is present in a nonuniform

---

[14]This field appears in any conductor moving through magnetic lines of force.

plasma, collisions are the only mechanism tending to equalize the concentration in the direction at right-angles to *H*. If the particles did not collide with each other, each of them could move freely only in the direction of the lines of force, that is, parallel to the direction of the magnetic field. The higher the temperature of the plasma, the lower the collision frequency, and therefore the lower the rate of diffusion. The diffusion coefficient for a fully ionized plasma in a transverse magnetic field is given by

$$D = A\frac{n}{H^2\sqrt{T_e}},\tag{7.7}$$

where the constant *A* is different for different substances. For hydrogen it is equal to about 0.014, while for helium it is 0.0035.

Figure 63 illustrates schematically the change in the concentration of plasma as a result of diffusion across the boundary between two regions with different values of n_e. It must be noted that, when we are concerned with the diffusion of plasma in a magnetic field, it is understood that the plasma as a whole is in motion rather than

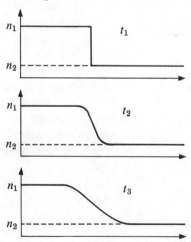

FIGURE 63. *Variation in the concentration of plasma as the result of diffusion at the boundary between two regions with different* n_e. *Three successive situations are illustrated.*

some small impurity within it. (This was assumed in the analysis of diffusion processes in the absence of the field.) This aspect represents a further fundamental difference between plasma processes occurring in the absence and in the presence of a field. When $H = 0$, a nonuniform distribution in the plasma pressure leads to a current rather than to diffusion. If the magnetic field strength is not zero, the difference in the plasma pressure is balanced by a corresponding difference in the electrodynamic pressure in such a way that the sum $p + H^2/8\pi$ is constant over the cross section of the plasma (provided that the lines of force are straight). Therefore, under these conditions, one should observe a gradual disappearance of the boundary between the regions of different values of p and a tendency towards a uniform spacial distribution of plasma.

The outward diffusion current from the region occupied by plasma leads to dispersion of the plasma which originally occupied a clearly defined region in a magnetic field, with the result that plasma eventually reaches the walls of the vessel. This phenomenon exhibits another aspect, namely, a decrease in the magnitude of the current flowing in the boundary layer of the plasma. We have already pointed out, in the preceding section, that this current is a direct consequence of the very existence of plasma confined by a magnetic field. The length of persistence of this current depends on the duration of the diffusion process. If there were no collisions between the particles, there would be no change in the configuration of the plasma in the plane perpendicular to H (since under these conditions $D = 0$). It follows that the current would remain constant. This result can obviously be related to the fact that, in the absence of collisions, the plasma behaves as a superconductor (since the electrical conductivity is proportional to the average time between collisions). By definition, the flow of current through a superconductor does not require an electromotive force to maintain the current.

The situation is quite different when collisions do take place. The diffusive dispersion of the plasma gives rise to a change in its concentration, and this, in its turn, leads to a change in the magnetic field inside the plasma (since with decreasing concentration there is a reduction in the diamagnetic effect, and therefore an increase in H). According to the law of induction, a change in the magnetic field passing through a plasma gives rise to an electromotive force which is responsible for maintaining the current in the plasma. It is easy to estimate the order of magnitude of the time necessary for the plasma to disperse in space as a result of diffusion. If the linear dimension, (for example, the diameter) of the region occupied by the plasma in the direction perpendicular to the field is L, the time necessary to retain the plasma in the magnetic field is given by $L \sim \sqrt{2Dt}$, and hence $t \sim L^2/D$.

Let us use this result to estimate the time during which a high-temperature plasma can be retained in the magnetic field of a thermonuclear reactor. Suppose that $L = 50$ cm, $T_e = T_i = 10^{8\,\circ}$K, $n_e = 10^{15}$ particles per cm^3, and $H = 10,000$ Oe. Under these conditions, the time interval in question turns out to be 180 sec.

In our previous analysis of the interaction of plasma with a magnetic field, we have been concerned mainly with those processes in which the plasma is a passive participant. However, in general, the plasma may also behave as an active factor affecting the field. This affects not only the diamagnetic properties of plasma, determined by the resultant electron and ion pressure but also, in the limiting case, leads to the complete exclusion of the field from the region occupied by the plasma. The effect of the plasma on the field may also be quite appreciable when the plasma as a whole moves rapidly across the lines of force, even if the gas-kinetic pressure $nk(T_e + T_i)$ is small in comparison with the magnetic pressure $H^2/8\pi$. The interaction is then due to the fact that the plasma behaves as a conductor in which an electromotive force, giving rise to a current, is produced as it moves through the magnetic field. The induced current gives rise to its own magnetic field and hence the initial magnetic field distribution is modified.

There is one further interesting property which characterizes the interaction of plasma with a magnetic field. Suppose that in a certain region of space the plasma and the magnetic field are completely intermingled, so that the magnetic field strength H and the plasma concentration n can, in principle, vary in an arbitrary manner from point to point. We shall confine our attention to the simple case where H and n vary only in the plane perpendicular to the lines of force, but remain constant along the lines of force. We can then imagine a filament of plasma in space, which is parallel to H and is thin enough so that H and n may be regarded as essentially constant. We shall suppose further that the plasma as a whole is moving across the magnetic lines of force. In all other respects, the motion will be assumed to be arbitrary. Our imaginary filament of plasma may have a variable cross section and may undergo compression and expansion, in which its cross-sectional area will decrease or increase. Accordingly, there may be a change in the concentration of the particles in a particular volume element. Suppose that, at the initial instant of time, the cross-sectional area of the filament of plasma is S_1 and the plasma concentration is n_1 so that the total number of particles per unit length is $n_1 S_1$. After a certain interval of time, the cross-sectional area will change and become equal to, say, S_2 while the concentration will be n_2. Since the total number of particles per unit length must remain constant, it follows that $n_1 S_1 = n_2 S_2$ and, therefore

$$\frac{n_1}{n_2} = \frac{S_2}{S_1}. \tag{7.8}$$

It must be noted that this result will only be valid if the motion of the plasma particles is collective in character, that is, if the plasma moves as a whole and the diffusion processes, tending to equalize the concentration at different points, may be ignored. This condition holds only for sufficiently rapid processes for which the time intervals under consideration are much smaller than the time necessary to retain the plasma in the magnetic field. For fast motion, the magnetic flux in each filament of the plasma is also conserved. The magnetic flux is equal to the product of the magnetic field H and the cross-sectional area S. The conservation of the magnetic flux in fast processes is a consequence of the law of induction, according to which a change in the magnetic flux through a conductor results in the appearance of an induced electromotive force. The latter gives rise to the current which produces a magnetic field tending to oppose the original change in the magnetic flux. The electromotive force is proportional to the rate of change of the flux while the current is, in addition, proportional to the conductivity of the material. Therefore, in sufficiently fast processes, that is, processes occurring over short intervals of time, even a small change in the magnetic field in a highly conducting plasma leads to a large instantaneous current, whose field compensates the increase or decrease in the flux. Therefore, in the case of fast plasma motion, Equation (7.8) is augmented by the further relation

$$S_1 H_1 = S_2 H_2, \tag{7.9}$$

showing that the magnetic flux remains constant. Hence, it follows that

$$\frac{H_1}{H_2} = \frac{S_2}{S_1}, \tag{7.10}$$

and comparison of Equations (7.8) and (7.10) yields

$$\frac{H_1}{H_2} = \frac{n_1}{n_2}. \tag{7.11}$$

Therefore, the magnetic field strength is proportional to the concentration, that is, the plasma density.

Moreover, it is clear that the ratio H/n remains constant for a given volume element. This characteristic feature of the interaction of plasma with a magnetic field is often referred to as the "freezing-in" of magnetic lines of force. This term is consistent with Faraday's model of a magnetic field, in which the lines of force are imagined to be real rather than conceptual. On this interpretation, the magnetic flux is measured by the number of lines of force passing through a given cross section of the plasma, and the fact that the flux is conserved means that these lines move together with the plasma just as if they were frozen into it. This idea has been very convenient and useful in the analysis of many phenomena involving conducting plasma in a magnetic field. However, its usefulness should not be overestimated. It is valid only if the deformation of the plasma occurs rapidly, and only in the direction perpendicular to H. Frozen-in magnetic lines of force are not peculiar to plasma. A similar effect occurs in the interaction between the magnetic field and any other good conductor.

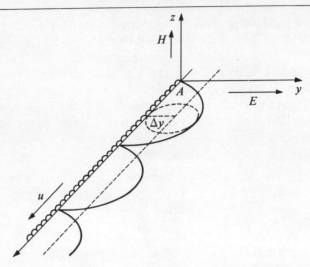

FIGURE 64. *Appearance of a plasma electric dipole moment in crossed electric and magnetic fields.*

A magnetic field has a very considerable effect on the dielectric properties of plasma. This may be understood with the aid of Fig. 64, which shows a layer of plasma in a uniform magnetic field. Suppose that an electric field parallel to the y axis is switched on with the result that the electrons and ions execute a cycloidal motion. The mean displacement along the y axis, from the initial position of each particle, is equal to one-half of the height of the cycloid. Displacement of the ions and electrons in opposite directions results in the formation of an excess positive charge on one side and excess negative charge on the other. The height of the cycloid is proportional to the mass of the particle, and therefore in calculating the amount of charge on the two surfaces, the displacement of the electrons may be ignored (in contrast to our earlier calculations of the permittivity of plasma in a high-frequency electric field with $H = 0$). The charges appearing on the boundaries of the plasma layer produce an additional electric field which is opposite to the external field E. This means that, when the electric and magnetic fields are perpendicular to each other, the plasma behaves as a dielectric with permittivity greater than unity. The permittivity of plasma in crossed electric and magnetic fields is given by

$$\epsilon_{mag} = 1 + \frac{4\pi\rho c^2}{H^2}, \tag{7.12}$$

where ρ is the density of the plasma; that is, $\rho = nm_i$. Provided the density is not too low, the permittivity ϵ_{mag} is practically always high Thus, for example, in hydrogen plasma with $n = 10^{13}$ particles per cm^3 and $H = 10,000$ Oe, the permittivity is found to be about 2,000. The large magnitude of ϵ_{mag} gives rise to some very interesting properties of the propagation of electromagnetic waves in magnetized plasma (see Section 7.5).

Equation (7.12) is not universally valid. It holds only when the electric field varies slowly. If the frequency of the field is comparable with the Larmor frequency of the ions, Equation (7.12) can no longer be used.

We shall use the above expression for ϵ_{mag} to analyze a fairly simple paradox concerned with the behavior of magnetized plasma in a gravitational field. Consider a plasma concentration in the form of a parallelepiped placed in a uniform magnetic field which is at right-angles to the gravitational field. At first sight, it would appear that the plasma will not fall since each charged particle will execute a drift motion at right-angles to both the gravitational and magnetic fields. However, it is evident from Fig. 64 that the drift motion leads to the appearance of equal and opposite charges on the surfaces of the condensation which, in turn, produce an electric field. This field also gives rise to a drift in the direction of the gravitational force. The drift of the particles under the action of the force mg takes place with the velocity $u = (c/eH)mg$. If the plasma concentration is n, the extra charge q formed on each square centimeter of the lateral surface of the plasma in a time t will be $n_e ut$ (only the drift of the ions is taken into account), so that

$$q = \frac{nm_i cgt}{H}. \tag{7.13}$$

According to the laws of electrostatics, the electric field inside the plasma due to these charges is equal to $4\pi q/\epsilon_{mag}$. If we now suppose that ϵ_{mag} is much greater than unity, we need only take the second term in Equation (7.12) and assume that $\epsilon_{mag} = 4\pi n m_i c^2/H^2$. The electric field in the plasma is then given by

$$E = \frac{4\pi q}{\epsilon_{mag}} = \frac{H}{c} gt,$$

and the drift velocity due to this field is

$$v = \frac{cE}{H} = gt \tag{7.14}$$

in agreement with the usual law of free fall.

7.4 The Pinch Effect

We shall now consider some specific examples of the interaction of plasma with magnetic fields which are of interest for the various possible applications of plasma physics. One such special case is the "pinch effect" which is observed in high-current gas discharges.

The passage of current through a gas discharge is associated with the appearance of electrodynamic forces acting on the ionized gas. The electrodynamic force $\mathbf{j} \times \mathbf{H}/c$ acting on a unit volume is always perpendicular to the direction of the current; that is, it tends to compress the plasma (see Fig. 59). One would therefore expect that in high-current electrical discharges the plasma will leave the walls and form a very narrow filament along the axis of the discharge tube. Let us suppose that there is equilibrium between the electro-dynamic forces which compress the plasma and the opposing gaseous pressure in the filament. We should then have a relatively simple relation between the temperature of the plasma and the current in the filament. We shall derive this relation under the following simplifying assumptions:

1. The current flows only over the surface of the filament of plasma. This should occur in discharges of short duration if the plasma exhibits high electrical conductivity, since the laws of electrodynamics predict that a high-frequency current does not penetrate into a conductor but flows only within a thin surface layer. This phenomenon is known as the "skin effect."

2. The temperature of the electrons and ions is the same and remains constant over the cross section of the filament.

3. The plasma filament is in the form of a cylinder of circular cross section.

It follows from the first assumption that the electrodynamic forces act on the surface layer of the filament and, since they must be balanced by the pressure, we have

$$p = \frac{H_I^2}{8\pi},\tag{7.15}$$

where H_I is the magnetic field due to the current at the outer surface of the filament. Since $T_e = T_i$, the pressure in the plasma is $2nkT$. The magnetic field strength due to the current on the surface of the filament is directly proportional to the current I and inversely proportional to the radius of the filament r_0. As is shown in textbooks on electricity and magnetism,

$$H_I = \frac{2I}{cr_0},\tag{7.16}$$

where c is the velocity of light and I is measured in electrostatic units. Substituting these expressions for p and H into (7.15), we have after some rearrangement

$$I^2 = 4c^2\pi r_0^2 nkT.\tag{7.17}$$

The quantity $\pi r_0^2 n$ is the number of particles of given sign per unit length of the plasma filament. We shall represent it by N. Equation (7.17) may then be rewritten in the form

$$I^2 = 4c^2 NkT.\tag{7.18}$$

If we now substitute the numerical value for k and express I in amperes (1 ampere = 3×10^9 esu), Equation (7.18) becomes

$$I_A^2 = 5.5 \cdot 10^{-14} NT,\tag{7.19}$$

which is more convenient for practical calculations.

The relation between I and T was derived above for a current flowing on the surface of the plasma filament. A more detailed theoretical analysis shows that this relationship remains valid for any distribution of current over the cross section of the plasma filament, provided only that the temperature is the same throughout.

Let us consider a concrete example which approaches the conditions obtaining in a real physical experiment concerned with the pinch effect. Suppose that the discharge tube is filled with hydrogen at an initial pressure of 0.1 mm Hg. The radius of the tube will be assumed to be equal to 10 cm and the discharge current will be taken as 5×10^5 amp. Under these conditions $N = \pi r_0^2 n = 2 \times 10^{18}$. The temperature of the plasma, as given by (7.19), will then be equal to two million degrees. This numerical example is interesting because it shows that it is possible, at least in principle, to achieve ultrahigh temperatures under laboratory conditions since it is quite easy to produce with modern apparatus a short current pulse of the order of 5×10^5 amp or even greater. The results of experimental studies of such high-current discharges will be dealt with in a later section.

The pinch effect, that is, the lateral compression of plasma by current passing through it, can also be achieved inductively by using a doughnut-shaped discharge tube and winding a coil on it. When the induced current is great enough, a circular filament of plasma is produced as before. However, as the cross-sectional area of the filament is reduced as a result of the pinch effect, there is also an increase in the radius of the current ring. The expansion of the

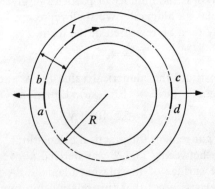

FIGURE 65. *Expansion of the current flowing in a ring.*

ring is due to the fact that each element of length of the ring experiences a force due to the magnetic fields of all the other elements. For example, the segment *ab* experiences the field due to the segment *cd*. Since the currents are equal and opposite, the two elements repel as indicated in Fig. 65. The current ring will therefore tend to expand, and its radius *R* will increase.

This property of the current ring is an example of a general result in electrodynamics: Namely, a conductor which carries a current always tends to increase its self-inductance. For a linear conductor, the increase in the self-inductance occurs when its length increases and the cross-sectional area decreases.

If there were no forces preventing the expansion of the ring, the

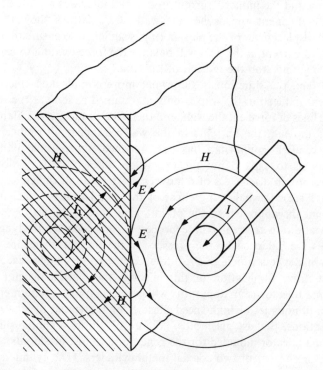

FIGURE 66. *"Image currents" produced in the conducting wall of a discharge chamber.*

plasma filament would eventually reach the outer wall of the chamber. However, under certain conditions, the forces which tend to expand the filament may be balanced. This occurs when the chamber is constructed from a metal with a high electrical conductivity. As the plasma ring expands, the magnetic lines of force due to it cut the walls of the chamber as shown in Fig. 66. This gives rise to an induced electromotive force which produces a current in the wall. The direction of this current is such as to prevent the penetration of the magnetic field into the wall. It follows that the direction of this current must be opposite to the direction of the current in the plasma, and therefore the two currents must repel each other. The force of repulsion between the current in the plasma and the induced current in the wall increases rapidly as the plasma filament approaches the wall. Calculations show that a small displacement of the plasma ring is sufficient to ensure that the induced current in the wall will balance the force tending to extend the ring, and stop the motion of the ring.

In fact, the situation is somewhat more complicated since the current induced in the wall is only maintained as long as the magnetic lines of force cut the wall, and therefore as soon as the filament stops moving, the currents in the wall disappear altogether. In reality, after equilibrium has been reached, the plasma filament continues to expand but the expansion takes place very slowly. Therefore, in discharges of relatively short duration (much smaller than 1 sec), the balancing effect of the metal wall is sufficient to prevent the approach of the plasma ring toward the wall.

In addition to steady-state processes, in which electrodynamic forces are balanced by the pressure in the plasma, there are also dynamic effects which give rise to acceleration of the plasma. The most direct application of this effect is the plasma injector. A plasma injector is an apparatus which injects into a vacuum either a continuous jet of high-speed plasma, or individual plasma condensations, that is, plasmoids. Figure 67 shows a simple pulsed plasma injector intended for the generation of fast plasmoids. The injector consists of two coaxial metal cylinders. The cylinders are fed by a capacitor bank which serves as a reservoir of electrical energy. A definite amount of gas is let into the space between the

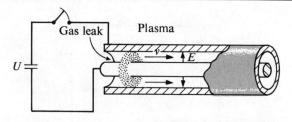

FIGURE 67. *Basic arrangement of a coaxial plasma injector.*

cylinders through a fast-acting inlet valve at a predetermined instant of time. Before the gas succeeds in expanding into the available space, the high voltage from the capacitor bank is applied to the electrodes and plasma is produced as a result of the electrical discharge. A current flows in the radial direction, and the interaction of the current with the magnetic field due to it gives rise to an electrodynamic pressure which accelerates the plasma along the injector. As a rough approximation, we can use Equation (7.4) and neglect the gas-kinetic pressure, that is, the term containing grad p. The larger the current passing through the plasma and the smaller the mass of the gas, the higher is the velocity reached by the plasmoid at the exit of the injector.

Devices of this type may be used under laboratory conditions to produce plasmoids accelerated to velocities of the order of a few hundred km per sec and containing 10^{18} to 10^{19} particles. Another example of a situation in which the interaction of plasma with a magnetic field is dynamic in character, is the deceleration of ionized gas in a magnetohydrodynamic converter. This new type of generator of electrical energy will be discussed in Section 8.2.

7.5 Oscillations and Waves in Plasma

Various forms of oscillations and waves may appear and propagate in plasma. They manifest themselves as a periodic variation in the charged-particle concentration and the electric or magnetic field strengths. One of the simplest processes of this kind, peculiar to plasma, is the Langmuir oscillations, illustrated in Fig. 68.

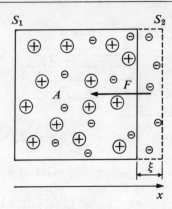

FIGURE 68. *Drawing illustrating the origin of Langmuir oscillations in plasma.*

Suppose that, in the volume A, the electrons have been displaced through a small distance ξ in the direction of the x axis. The reason for this displacement is unimportant for our purposes and may in fact be quite accidental. As a result of the displacement of the electrons to the right, electrical charges will appear on the surfaces S_1 and S_2 which bound the region A; these charges produce an electric field which tends to return the electrons to their original position.

The resulting force may be compared with the force acting on a pendulum and tending to return it to its position of equilibrium. In both cases, the restoring force is proportional to the deflection and gives rise to periodic oscillations. The dependence of the deflection on time can then be represented by a sine curve, and the frequency of the oscillations, that is, their number per second, is given by

$$\nu_0 = \frac{1}{2\pi}\sqrt{\frac{f}{m}}, \qquad (7.20)$$

where f is the elastic constant, that is, the ratio of the force to the deflection, and m is the mass of the body executing the oscillations. This formula is valid for any process in which the restoring force is proportional to the displacement. In particular, in the case of electron oscillations in plasma,[15] the force is given by

$$F = eE = 4\pi ne^2\xi. \tag{7.21}$$

Therefore

$$f = 4\pi ne^2$$

and

$$\nu_0 = \frac{\omega_0}{2\pi} = \sqrt{\frac{ne^2}{\pi m_e}} = 9 \cdot 10^3 \sqrt{n_e}. \tag{7.22}$$

We recall that we have already encountered this quantity in a somewhat different context. According to Equation (5.11), it represents the critical frequency of electromagnetic waves, that is, the minimum value of the frequency at which electromagnetic waves can penetrate into plasma.

The oscillations of plasma ions are somewhat more complicated. Owing to the much greater mass of the ions, these oscillations are slower and therefore the electrons, which follow the ions but have a much greater mobility, compensate almost completely the electric fields produced as a result of such oscillations. We shall not consider in detail the mechanism of ion oscillations and will merely note that their propagation through plasma is analogous to the propagation of sound through a neutral gas. If there is thermal equilibrium between the electrons and ions in the plasma, that is, if $T_e \approx T_i$, this "ion sound" propagates with a velocity of the order of the thermal velocity of the ions. When T_e is much greater than T_i, the velocity of propagation of the sound is found to be of the order of $\sqrt{kT_e/m_i}$; that is, the sound wave travels with the velocity which the ions would have if their temperature were equal to the electron temperature. Theoretical analysis shows that plasma sound waves can propagate freely in the latter case, that is, when the ions are much colder than the electrons. If, on the other hand, the velocity of sound is of the order of the thermal velocity of the ions, which should occur when $T_i \approx T_e$, the sound waves will be rapidly at-

[15]The electric field inside the region A is equal to $4\pi q$, where q is the charge per unit area on S_1 or S_2. Electrons displaced through a distance ξ produce an extra charge of $q = ne\xi$.

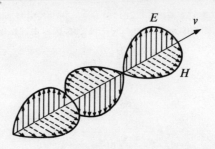

FIGURE 69. *Electric and magnetic fields in a transverse electromagnetic wave.*

tenuated in the plasma; that is, their energy will be absorbed and converted into heat. Under these conditions, the sound can only propagate through plasma over very short distances.

The Langmuir electron oscillations and ion sound are forms of periodic motion of matter in the longitudinal direction. This motion gives rise to longitudinal electric fields. However, ordinary electromagnetic waves can also propagate through plasma. Let us recall some of the main properties of such waves: In their simplest form, electromagnetic waves are a periodic process in which the electric and magnetic fields are strictly related to each other. In vacuum, the velocity of propagation of electromagnetic waves is always the same and equal to c. Both the electric and magnetic fields in the wave are perpendicular to the direction of propagation; that is, the waves are transverse oscillations of the two components of the electromagnetic field as illustrated in Fig. 69. In a material medium, the velocity of propagation of electromagnetic waves is $c/\sqrt{\epsilon}$, where ϵ is the permittivity. In the absence of a magnetic field the permittivity of plasma is less than unity, and therefore the velocity of propagation of electromagnetic waves in plasma is greater than the velocity of light in a vacuum. Electromagnetic waves cannot penetrate into plasma and propagate in it if their frequency is less than ν_0, since the permittivity is then negative and the velocity of the wave complex.

The propagation of electromagnetic waves in magnetized plasma is of particular interest. The phenomenon is very complicated and a detailed analysis would be neither easy nor useful within the framework of this book. We shall, therefore, confine our attention to a general description of a few important special cases. To begin with, it must be noted that the magnetic field should have no appreciable effect on the passage of an electromagnetic field through plasma if the frequency of the waves is much greater than the Larmor frequency. The oscillations of the electrons are then so fast that the magnetic field has no chance to affect them, and therefore the permittivity of plasma is the same as when $H = 0$. The opposite case occurs when the frequency is very low. If it is much lower than the Larmor frequency of the plasma ions, the propagation of electromagnetic waves through plasma exhibits some very special features. The simplest result is obtained when the direction of propagation is parallel to the direction of the constant magnetic field H_0. The alternating electric and magnetic fields in the wave are then perpendicular to H_0 (Fig. 70) and the field strength at each point in space is the vector sum of H_0 and the alternating field in the wave. As a result, the lines of force assume a wave-like form, and since they are frozen into the medium, their deformation brings the plasma into motion, so that it takes part in the oscillation. A large proportion of the electromagnetic energy associated with the wave is thus converted into the kinetic energy of oscillation of the medium. Therefore, the velocity of propagation of electromagnetic waves in a dense plasma should be much smaller than the velocity of electromagnetic waves in vacuum. The situation is somewhat similar to the propagation of elastic waves along a wire. If the density, that is, the mass per unit length, is higher at some point along the wire than elsewhere, the velocity of the wave is reduced

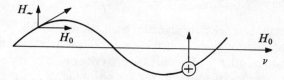

FIGURE 70. *Distortion of a magnetic line of force (the curved line) due to the propagation of an electromagnetic wave, carrying an alternating magnetic field $H_\sim$, in the direction of a constant magnetic field H_0.*

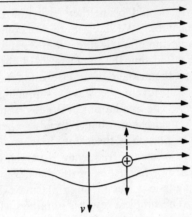

FIGURE 71. *Propagation of a sound wave in magnetized plasma. The wave is associated with the bending of the lines of force.*

accordingly. In the propagation of electromagnetic waves in the direction of a constant magnetic field in plasma, the lines of force act as elastic threads along which oscillations are transmitted. These threads are "loaded" by the plasma, and therefore the velocity of the wave is reduced.

The change in the velocity of electromagnetic waves in plasma can also be predicted in a more formal way by considering the permittivity of magnetized plasma (Section 7.2). In a dense plasma located in a magnetic field, the permittivity is equal to $4\pi pc^2/H^2$ (see Equation (7.12)), and therefore the velocity of propagation in the direction of the magnetic field is given by

$$u = \frac{c}{\sqrt{\epsilon}} = \frac{H}{\sqrt{4\pi p}}. \tag{7.23}$$

Such transverse electromagnetic oscillations, which propagate along the lines of force as if these were elastic threads, are called Alfven waves, after the Swedish astrophysicist who predicted them.

The properties of sound waves are also modified in the case of magnetized plasma. In a sound wave, the oscillations of the medium occur in the direction of propagation, and therefore a magnetic field frozen into the plasma may have an important effect on the propagation of the waves when they travel at right-angles to the lines of force. This is different from the case of electromagnetic waves which are, of course, transverse in character. The propagation of a sound wave through magnetized plasma is illustrated schematically in Fig. 71. It is connected with the periodically varying bending of the lines of force. If the temperature of the plasma is not too high, the velocity of propagation of such waves is also given by (7.23); that is, it is equal to the velocity of Alfven waves. A sound wave propagating at right-angles to the magnetic lines of force in plasma can be excited, for example, by applying a rapid periodic variation to the magnetic field near the boundary of the plasma.

In addition to the simple special cases which we have discussed above, there are also other forms of oscillatory and wave processes which can develop in plasma. Further discussion of these problems is beyond the scope of this book.

8

Technological Applications

8.1 Controlled Thermonuclear Reactions

The current trend in plasma research has been to concentrate on those topics which are likely to lead to useful practical applications. The most important of these is the utilization of the enormous quantities of energy which are stored in the nuclei of the very abundant light elements. Although the problem is still largely unsolved, its importance is so great, and it is so intimately connected with the development of plasma physics, that the technological applications of plasma are virtually inseparable from it.

In contrast to the nuclei of such heavy elements as uranium or thorium, whose energy can be released in the fission process, that is, division into lighter fragments under neutron bombardment, the nuclei of light elements can give up their energy only in synthetic processes, in which two colliding nuclei fuse and form a heavier nucleus. One of the simplest examples of such a synthetic reaction is the fusion of deuterium nuclei which results in the formation of helium or tritium.[16] This nuclear reaction may be written in the form

$$H^2 + H^2 \begin{cases} \to He^3 + n^1 \\ \to H^3 + H^1, \end{cases} \tag{8.1}$$

when n^1 is a neutron, H^1, H^2, H^3 represent the three isotopes of hydrogen, and He^3 represents the helium isotope of atomic weight 3.

---

[16]We recall that deuterium is the hydrogen isotope with atomic weight 2, while tritium is the hydrogen isotope with atomic weight 3.

The two arrows show that a collision between two deuterons may result in the appearance of either a helium nucleus and a neutron, or a tritium nucleus and a proton. In the first case, the energy released in the fusion reaction is about 3.3 MeV (MeV = million electron-volts), while in the second case, the energy is about 4 MeV. When the masses involved in the reactions are the same, the energy released in the fusion process is found to be approximately the same as the fission energy released in uranium reactors. However, the conditions which must be obtained before the reactions can take place are quite different in the two cases. Fission can occur in a medium whose atoms are at rest, since atomic nuclei play a passive role and are simply targets for the bombarding neutrons. In contrast, the fusion reaction can only occur in a medium whose nuclei are in very rapid motion. The basic fusion reaction can only occur when the two interacting particles approach each other to within a distance of the order of 10^{-13} cm. This can only happen if they overcome their mutual electrostatic repulsion, that is, if they have a very high relative velocity. This in its turn means that the temperature of the medium must be very high. It follows that the necessary condition for the fusion reaction to proceed at a high rate is that the medium must be very hot. Hence the term *thermonuclear reaction*.

Calculations show that fusion reactions of the type described by Equation (8.1) occur at an appreciable rate only above temperatures of the order of a few million degrees but in order that the liberated energy be of practical interest, the temperature of the deuterium must be increased to a few hundred million degrees. At such temperatures, the deuterium can, of course, no longer exist as a neutral medium and is converted into highly ionized plasma consisting of fast deuterons and electrons. It is evident that the main difficulty lies in the insulation of the high-temperature plasma from the walls of the chamber in which it is contained. Since plasma has an enormous thermal conductivity, this insulation is essential, because otherwise all the energy would immediately escape to the walls and the required high temperature would not be reached. This means that the plasma must, in effect, be contained in a high vacuum, and this can only be achieved with the aid of a magnetic field whose lines of force surround the plasma. In point of fact, the idea of magnetic thermal insulation of plasma is contained in Equation (7.2).

In the Soviet Union, this idea was first used in connection with controlled thermonuclear fusion by A. D. Sakharov and I. Ye. Tamm in 1950. Similar work was performed independently and at the same time in Great Britain and the U.S.A. However, most of the work was classified at the time, and therefore there was no exchange of information.

The idea of magnetic thermal insulation led to a very rapid development of experimental studies in the Soviet Union. Initially, the experimental work was based on use of the pinch effect. As has already been pointed out in the preceding chapter, the passage of a high current through plasma gives rise to a compression of the medium by the resulting electrodynamic force. This removes the plasma from the vicinity of the walls of the discharge tube and confines it to the central region. The electric current performs three functions: (1) in the initial stage it produces the plasma by ionization; (2) the electrodynamic forces due to it maintain the plasma in a compressed state, and (3) it heats the plasma to a very high temperature as a result of the liberation of Joule heat. The simple example illustrated by Equation (7.3) shows that, with relatively modest and easily realizable initial conditions, it is quite possible to heat deuterium plasma to a temperature of many million degrees, and hence produce thermonuclear reactions at an appreciable rate. However, it was soon shown experimentally that the rather optimistic original estimates were not entirely justified. It has been found that the plasma filament, produced as a result of the pinch effect, is very unstable. The geometry of the filament is radically altered within a few millionths of a second as a result of this instability. The result is that the heated plasma is splashed onto the walls of the discharge tube, and the very high temperature reached during the initial stages of the process, as the plasma is pinched by the electrodynamic forces, exists only for an exceedingly short interval of time.

In the early experiments performed in the Soviet Union, the maximum current in the plasma during the discharge pulse was 10^5 to 10^6 amperes and the rise time of the current from zero to its maximum value was 5 to 10 microseconds. The initial pressure of the deuterium, which was the main substance used in these early experiments, was usually between a few hundredths and a few tenths of a millimeter of mercury. Under these initial conditions, the process developed as follows. At first, the plasma was found to pinch very rapidly. In the final stage of this process, the temperature of the plasma filament was of the order of a million degrees, or even a few million degrees. As soon as the pinch process is over, the plasma cord executes very rapid radial oscillations: The ring alternately expands and contracts. During this stage, the instability of the filament sets in and gives rise to an interaction of the plasma with the walls, leading to the contamination of the deuterium by impurities and to rapid cooling. All this occurs within a few microseconds. When the current reaches its maximum value, the temperature of the plasma is already much lower than that during the initial stages of the pinch effect. Successive stages in the development of the plasma filament are illustrated in Fig. 72. Each of the photographs corresponds to a 0.5 microsecond exposure and the separation between the photographs is roughly of the same order.

The thermonuclear reaction yield produced under these conditions is, of course, rather modest. The observed short burst of neutrons, which is of the order of a few tenths of a microsecond, is in fact due to the acceleration of a small group of very fast deuterons by the electric fields developed in the plasma as a result of its strong instability, rather than the thermonuclear reactions. Although this phenomenon is interesting in itself, and was certainly unexpected, it does not resolve the main practical problem, since it involves only a small proportion of the available number of particles and gives rise to a very brief train of nuclear reactions.

The results of these experiments soon led to the following crucial question: Under what conditions will magnetically supported hot plasma remain stable? Clearly, the answer to this question will govern the successful utilization of controlled thermonuclear reaction. In spite of a very large number of theoretical calculations, the question is still an open one. We are not yet absolutely certain that there are states in which a dense hot plasma, completely

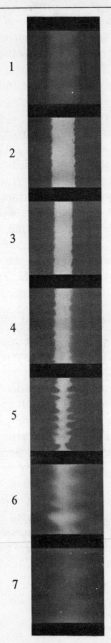

FIGURE 72. *Photograph of seven successive stages in the development of a plasma filament in a pinching discharge. The frames are separated by 5×10^{-7} seconds*

separated from the walls and supported by magnetic forces in a vacuum, will remain in equilibrium for a sufficiently long interval of time. The phrase "sufficiently long" is used in the sense that during the existence of the hot plasma, each deuteron should have an appreciable chance of entering into a nuclear reaction. At present, the development of methods for producing and maintaining high-temperature plasma is intimately connected with investigations of the stability of various plasma configurations. We must therefore consider the problem of stability before we proceed to the more general problem of thermonuclear fusion.

Let us return, therefore, to the consideration of a plasma filament through which a current is flowing. In order to exhibit the main physical features of the phenomenon, we shall simplify the problem by assuming that the plasma is perfectly conducting. As a result of the skin effect, the current will then be confined to a thin surface layer. Figs. 73 and 74 show two simple kinds of deformation of a cylindrical column of plasma which are produced by random fluctuations. In the first case, there is a local reduction in the radius of the cylinder. Since for a given current the magnetic field at the surface of the plasma is inversely proportional to the radius of the cylinder, it follows that the field in the plane ab must be greater than the field at the undeformed surface. Therefore, the magnetic pressure $H^2/8\pi$

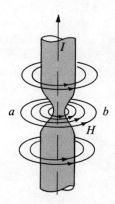

FIGURE 73. *Local contraction of a plasma filament.*

which compresses the plasma in the deformed region, must also be greater in this region. Since, however, the pressure p in the plasma must be the same throughout (since the plasma can flow freely along the cylinder), it follows that in the region of contraction, the equilibrium between electrodynamic and plasma pressures is upset and a small initial deformation will increase rapidly. This means that the plasma cylinder is unstable with respect to local changes in its diameter.

In the case of deformations of the form illustrated in Fig. 74, the magnetic field strength is different on opposite sides of the bent segment. On the outer (convex) side, it is reduced, while on the inner (concave), it is increased. There is, therefore, a difference in the magnetic pressures in the direction *ab* and this leads to a rapid increase in the initial deformation. It follows that the plasma cylinder is also unstable with respect to bending. This form of instability is particularly dangerous from the point of view of thermal insulation of plasma since it eventually leads to contact between the plasma and the wall. These two forms of instability are not exclusive to plasma — they are equally characteristic of any linear conductor carrying a current, or any medium which is not rigid, that is, which does not oppose changes in its form.

Having discovered the possible instabilities of a plasma conductor, we must now consider how we can stabilize it. This can be done through the aid of additional external magnetic fields which are independent of the field due to the plasma current itself. Suppose, for example, that a coil has been wound on the outer surface of the discharge tube and is used to produce a strong magnetic field whose lines of force are parallel to the current in the plasma

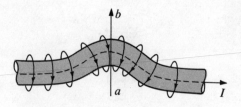

FIGURE 74. *Bending of a plasma filament.*

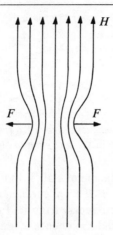

FIGURE 75. *Compression of the magnetic lines of force of a longitudinal magnetic field during a local contraction of a current-carrying column of plasma.*

(Fig. 56). As explained in the preceding chapter, properties characteristic of elastic rubber bands may be ascribed to the magnetic lines of force. They are compressed in the transverse direction and stretched in the longitudinal direction, and therefore tend to contract longitudinally and expand laterally. These two properties may be used as a stabilizing factor opposing the deformation of a cylinder of plasma. A local contraction of the form illustrated in Fig. 75 gives rise to a compression of the lines of force within the plasma conductor, and therefore the magnetic pressure in the plasma increases. In contrast, the density of the lines of force outside the cylinder is reduced, and therefore the magnetic pressure due to the longitudinal field is also reduced. This gives rise to a magnetic pressure gradient which leads to the return of the plasma conductor to its original form (if the longitudinal field is high enough).

In the case of bending (Fig. 76), the lines of force associated with the longitudinal field are stretched and this leads to the appearance of a force F tending to reduce the bending. A conducting metal envelope can also be used as a means of enhancing the longitudinal field. As has already been pointed out earlier, when the plasma

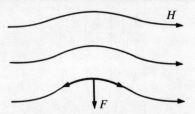

FIGURE 76. *Stretching of magnetic lines of force during the bending of a current-carrying column of plasma.*

conductor approaches the metal wall, it induces a current within it, and the two currents repel. This phenomenon reduces the tendency of the plasma filament to depart from its axial position in the discharge chamber, when the chamber is made out of metal or is surrounded by a metal envelope.

These methods of reducing the instabilities are being used at the present time in installations designed for the study of high-temperature plasma. An installation of this kind is illustrated in Fig. 77.

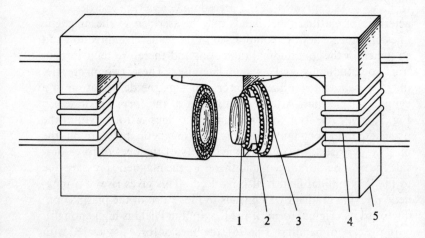

FIGURE 77. *Toroidal discharge chamber with a longitudinal magnetic field: 1 — inner chamber or liner, 2 — outer copper chamber, 3 — coil producing the magnetic field 4 — primary of transformer (the plasma filament acts as the secondary), 5 — iron core.*

The discharge chamber is toroidal in form and surrounds the iron core of a transformer. The current in the gas is excited inductively and the circular plasma filament, which is produced during the discharge, acts as the secondary of the transformer. The plasma filament is stabilized by means of the longitudinal magnetic field due to the coil wound on the outer surface of the chamber.

The chamber itself is usually of the two-layer kind. The plasma is produced inside a thin, corrugated stainless-steel shell, 0.2 to 0.3 mm thick. This thin inner chamber is known as the *liner* and is inserted into a thick copper envelope. The space between the liner and the outer envelope is evacuated to a very low pressure. This design ensures that the experiments can be carried out under very clean vacuum conditions since the liner can be baked, by passing a current through it, and thus thoroughly degassed. Experimental installations of this kind have been developed in the Soviet Union and are collectively referred to as "Tokamak" installations. The biggest of these is designed to produce currents up to $2.5-3 \times 10^5$ amperes with a stabilizing longitudinal field of up to 4,000 oersteds. In the Tokamak installations, the plasma filament exists for 0.005–0.02 seconds. So far, maximum temperatures of the order of two million degrees have been achieved.

It is still difficult to prophesy the final maximum temperatures which it will be possible to produce by heating the plasma with a current. The stability of the plasma filament is also an unresolved problem. Although all the measurements indicate that the Tokamak installations produce relatively stable rings of plasma, if the longitudinal magnetic field is high enough, absolute stability has not been achieved. There is also a further form of instability which leads to the gradual spread of the plasma filament as a result of a process which may be referred to as *anomalous diffusion*. The latter is due to the fact that plasma is capable of diffusing at right-angles to the lines of force much more rapidly than predicted by the classical laws of diffusion in a magnetic field.

Recent theoretical studies have unearthed a number of processes which may be responsible for anomalous diffusion. They all involve the same physical mechanism, that is, the excitation of various forms of plasma oscillations due to the transfer of energy from directed beams of plasma particles. The directed motion of one of the components of plasma relative to another, that is, the motion of electrons relative to the ions, is nothing else than an electric current. We have seen in the preceding chapter that such currents can exist in plasma in a magnetic field (even in the absence of external electromotive forces). The excitation of oscillations in plasma by a directed beam of particles is, in a sense, analogous to the excitation of sea waves by the wind, except for the important distinction that the wind produces surface waves, while the electrical wind in the plasma gives rise to three-dimensional waves.

It should be noted that a directed beam of particles passing through plasma can only excite plasma waves which propagate with a velocity of the order of the velocity of the beam itself. The oscillations and waves produced in plasma give rise to electric fields which may have components at right-angles to H. This, in its turn, is responsible for a drift motion at right-angles to the magnetic lines of force, that is, the anomalous diffusion mentioned above. It is still not clear whether the anomalously high rate of diffusion is an unavoidable feature of the circular rings of plasma which are produced in installations of the kind we have discussed so far. It may be that when the longitudinal magnetic field is very much greater than the field due to the current in the plasma, all the minor instabilities, including anomalous diffusion, will be suppressed. If this optimistic assumption turns out to be right, it might be possible to heat the plasma to temperatures of the order of ten million degrees. A plasma ring with a concentration of the order of 10^{13} to 10^{14} particles per cm^3 would be a relatively powerful source of thermonuclear reactions.

The pinch effect is not the only way of insulating a high-temperature plasma. The plasma may be prevented from coming into contact with the walls of the chamber by means of an externally produced magnetic field. Systems of this kind, in which the thermal insulation is achieved with the aid of external magnetic fields, are known as magnetic traps. Simple forms of magnetic traps are illustrated in Figs. 15 and 78. The first of these two figures shows a system with two magnetic mirrors and has been described in Chapter 2. In Fig. 15, the magnetic field increases in the axial

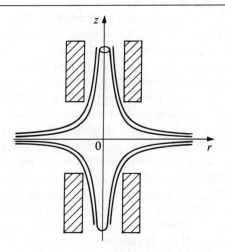

FIGURE 78. *Magnetic trap with opposing fields (the coils producing the field are represented by the rectangles).*

direction on either side of the central region. Plasma particles travelling at a large angle to the lines of force will be trapped and will not succeed in leaving the system. A plasma captured in a trap of this kind will occupy the spindle-shaped central region.

We note that, even if all the stability conditions are satisfied, the plasma will be retained by the trap for a long interval of time only if its temperature is very high and its density very low. A single collision is sufficient to ensure that the direction of a particle is changed, so that it may succeed in escaping from the trap. Therefore, it is necessary that the collision frequency be small, and this can only occur at high temperatures or very low concentrations. The second magnetic system (Fig. 78) differs from the first in that the magnetic fields due to the two coils are in opposite directions. As a result, the lines of force in the space between the two coils are deflected away from the axis, rather like the bristles of two shaving brushes pressed against each other. The field strength at the central point 0 is zero. In the neighborhood of this point, the magnitude of H increases, both in the axial and radial directions, in proportion to the distance from 0. In this system, the plasma occupies a volume which has the form of a spinning top. This magnetic trap will retain particles for which the angle between the direction of motion and the lines of force is not too small.

Since the external magnetic field in these magnetic traps serves only as the thermal insulator, the problem of heating the plasma is quite independent of the trapping problem. It can be resolved in various ways; for example, it is possible to inject into the trap plasmoids, accelerated to high velocities with the aid of electro-dynamic injectors of the kind described in the preceding chapter. However, the most important problem is not the development of methods for filling up magnetic traps with plasma, but the elucida-tion of the conditions under which stable retention of hot plasma in the trap is possible.

The first of the above mentioned two traps presents the most serious difficulties as far as stability is concerned. This system has one obvious disadvantage: The magnetic field decreases in the radial direction, that is, at right-angles to the axis. Since the plasma exhibits diamagnetic properties, and therefore tends to move in the direction of decreasing magnetic field, it follows that if a small pimple or hump appears on the surface of the plasma, it will tend to grow in the radial direction. As a result, random surface deforma-tion will lead to the appearance of streaks of plasma whose length will continuously increase. This will eventually result in the expan-sion of the plasma, bringing it into contact with the walls.

A similar conclusion can be reached by considering the variation of the ratio of plasma pressure to the magnetic pressure during a deformation of the surface of the plasma. Let us suppose, for the sake of simplicity, that the magnetic field in the plasma is zero. Under these conditions, we have $p = H^2/8\pi$ on the boundary be-tween the plasma and the field. If a small section of the surface is deformed so that it enters a region of lower field strength, the equilibrium of the forces is upset, and the pressure in the plasma will no longer be balanced by the electrodynamic force. Therefore, the deformation will tend to increase. These qualitative conclusions are supported by detailed theoretical calculations and are in agree-ment with the experimental results. In spite of the large number of attempts at achieving stable retention of plasma within mirror traps, and a number of premature reports that this has been achieved, in reality nobody has succeeded in maintaining pure hydrogen plasma at high ion temperature in a magnetic trap for more than a few tenths of a microsecond.

Traps of the kind illustrated in Fig. 78 do not suffer from the above disadvantage, since they are characterized by an increase in the magnetic field strength in all directions away from the central region which is filled with plasma. Therefore, as far as surface deformations are concerned, this configuration should be stable. However, theory shows that systems of this kind suffer from another kind of defect. It is found that the plasma flows out through the sharp edge of the region occupied by it, that is, through the boundary of the plane of symmetry of the plasma confined in the trap. This difficulty is directly related to the fact that the trap contains a region in which the field strength passes through zero and therefore $W_\perp/H$ does not remain constant for particles entering this region. In the neighborhood of the region where the field is zero, there is no unique relation between the direction of motion of the particles and the direction of the lines of force. It follows that the condition for the retention of the particles in the trap, which requires that the angle between the velocity and the magnetic field must be large, breaks down. A particle passing through this region has an appreciable probability of changing its direction of motion relative to the lines of force and leaving the plasma at a small angle to the direction of H (if it moves near the plane of symmetry of the magnetic system). This theoretical conclusion has not yet been confirmed experimentally but there is little doubt that it is correct.

It would appear therefore that the most suitable configurations ensuring efficient thermal insulation of high-temperature plasma are traps with composite magnetic fields, combining the properties of the systems illustrated in Figs. 15 and 78 but free of their basic defects. In such magnetic systems the magnetic field should not go to zero anywhere in the region occupied by the plasma, whilst the magnitude of H should increase in the outward direction. A magnetic system satisfying these requirements is illustrated in Fig. 79. The field is produced by two coils with six linear, current-carrying conductors disposed symmetrically relative to the line

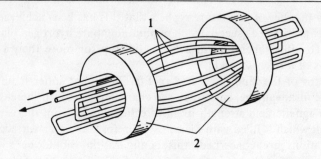

FIGURE 79. *Magnetic trap with composite fields: 1 — additional current-carrying conductors, 2 — main coils.*

joining the centers of the two coils. In the absence of the conductors, the system would form a simple magnetic trap of the form previously illustrated in Fig. 15. However, the additional conductors carry currents which flow in directions normal in the plane perpendicular to the axis and produce a field whose magnitude increases with the distance r from the axis. In particular, for a system consisting of six such conductors, the field H near the axis increases in proportion to r^2. This magnetic trap was used in the first successful experiment in which high-temperature plasma was maintained in a stable configuration for time intervals of the order of a tenth of a second.

Although an interval of time of the order of one-tenth of a second seems rather short in comparison to the time intervals encountered in every-day life, it is nevertheless very long in comparison to the time intervals which characterize the development of microprocesses in plasma. For example, a fast electron in hot plasma may succeed in traversing the plasma several hundred times in one-tenth of a second, and the corresponding path length in the plasma will exceed 100 km. This means that one-tenth of a second represents a satisfactory retension of the particles in the plasma. This result was achieved by M. S. Ioffe in the Department of Plasma Studies of the Institute of Atomic Energy of the USSR, and is the major achievement in the development of controlled thermonuclear reactions in recent years.

It is, of course, still too early to say that the way is now open to the successful utilization of thermonuclear generators of energy. So far, it has only been possible to retain the plasma particles in a magnetic field at relatively low concentrations and it is still not known what will be the behavior of *dense* plasma under these conditions. It must also be remembered that there are still no effective methods of producing high-temperature plasma of high concentration. However, one gains the impression that one of the main barriers to the successful development of thermonuclear generators has been removed and that technological developments will finally lead to a successful solution of this problem. Thermonuclear fusion will then become an important new source of energy available for the requirements of mankind.

8.2 Magnetohydrodynamic Conversion of Energy

Let us now briefly consider other possible applications of plasma processes in the near future. We shall consider only those which are promising enough to justify extensive research. The first of these applications is concerned with direct transformation of thermal energy into electrical energy. The basic idea is quite simple. A jet of ionized gas, in which a large proportion of the initial store of energy is transformed into the kinetic energy of directed motion, is injected into a magnetic field at right-angles to the lines of force (Fig. 80). When the plasma jet intersects the lines of force, an

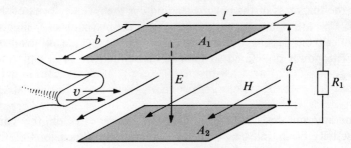

FIGURE 80. *Basic arrangement of a magnetohydrodynamic converter (the nozzle is on the left).*

electromotive force is induced in the plasma. The magnitude of the induced electric field E is equal to vH/c, where v is the velocity of the plasma jet. The induced electric field gives rise to an electric current which flows at right-angles to both v and H and is allowed to pass through the external load R_1. The load is connected across the electrodes A_1 and A_2, which are in contact with the plasma jet.

An installation based on this idea is known as a magnetohydrodynamic generator. The electrical energy liberated in the external circuit of the generator is taken at the expense of the kinetic energy of the plasma jet, so that the jet is decelerated as a result of the interaction between the current flowing in the plasma and the magnetic field. The force per unit volume of the moving plasma is equal to jH/c, and therefore the work done in displacing the unit volume through a distance l is equal to jHl/c. It follows that the change in the kinetic energy per unit volume must also be equal to this quantity. The work done by the electrodynamic force is, in fact, the source of energy for the entire electric circuit. Let the resistance in the external circuit be R_1 and the internal resistance of the region between the electrodes be R_2. The current flowing through the magnetodydrodynamic generator is then given by Ohm's law

$$I = \frac{U}{R_1 + R_2}. \tag{8.2}$$

If all the quantities in this formula are expressed in practical units, then $U = 10^{-8} \, vH\alpha$, where α is the gap between the electrodes, that is, the thickness of the plasma jet, and v is the mean velocity of the jet. (We are assuming that the velocity of the plasma is only slightly reduced on passing through the gap defined by the electrodes.)

The power dissipated in the external circuit is

$$W = I^2 R_1 = \frac{U^2 R_1}{(R_1 + R_2)^2}. \tag{8.3}$$

The internal resistance of the generator depends on the conductivity of the plasma η and the geometrical dimensions of the system, and is given by

$$R_2 = \frac{1}{\eta} \cdot \frac{d}{bl}, \tag{8.4}$$

where b is the width of the plasma jet and l the length of the electrodes, that is, the length of the region in which the plasma is decelerated. It is assumed that the magnetic field is uniform over the entire area bl. For a given set of parameters defining the geometric dimensions of the generator and properties of the plasma jet, the maximum transfer of energy (although not the maximum efficiency) corresponds to $R_1 = R_2$. Under these conditions

$$W = 10^{-16} \frac{\eta v^2 H^2 \Omega}{4}, \tag{8.5}$$

where $\Omega = dbl$ represents the working volume in which the kinetic energy of the jet is converted into electrical energy. The efficiency with which the energy is converted is proportional to $\eta v^2 H^2$. Therefore, in order to increase the efficiency, both the conductivity and the velocity of the plasma jet must be increased. It must be noted that Equation (8.5) was derived under highly simplifying assumptions and can only be used for very approximate estimates of the electrical power. It cannot, of course, be used as a practical formula in the theoretical design of magnetohydrodynamic generators.

Some idea about the orders of magnitude involved in the operation of magnetohydrodynamic generators may be obtained as follows: Suppose that $v = 10^5$ cm per sec, $H = 2,000$ Oe and $d = 100$ cm. Under these conditions, the electromotive force U is equal to 2,000 V. If the resistivity of the plasma is of the order of 1 ohm cm, $b = 10$ cm, and $l = 100$ cm, Equation (8.5) shows that, when the external and internal resistances are equal, the power released in the external load is about 10,000 kVa.

So far, we have confined our attention to the motion of a plasma jet in a magnetic field because the principle of the magnetohydrodynamic converter is based on this process. However, it is evident that the converter must also incorporate certain other elements. The original form of the energy is the thermal energy of the gas, given to it either by a combustion process or by heating the material by nuclear radiation, for example, in a nuclear reactor. The first requirement is therefore to transform the energy of random thermal motion into the energy of a directed beam. This can be done by allowing the heated gas to expand into a vacuum through a specially designed gas-dynamic nozzle (see Fig. 80). In an expansion of this kind, no work is done against external forces and the thermal energy of the gas is simply transformed into the kinetic energy of the directed beam. Therefore, if the temperature in the thermal reservoir (inside the nuclear reactor or in ordinary space) is equal to T_1, it will be reduced to T_2 at the mouth of the nozzle. Consider an element of unit mass in the jet. The initial store of heat in this element is $C_T T_1$, where C_T is the specific heat. After expansion, the thermal energy is reduced to $C_T T_2$. The difference between these two quantities is equal to the kinetic energy of directed motion which for our element of unit mass is equal to $\frac{1}{2}v^2$. Therefore, the velocity of the beam leaving the nozzle is given by

$$v = \sqrt{2C_T(T_1 - T_2)}.$$

However, it is not enough to produce a directed beam of rapidly moving gas. It is also necessary to ensure that the jet should have a sufficiently high degree of ionization, since otherwise it will not be an adequate conductor of electricity.

The production of highly conducting ionized jets is one of the main problems at the present stage of development of magneto-hydrodynamic converters. In principle, this can easily be done if there were no practical limits to the initial temperature of the gas. In fact, at a sufficiently high temperature T_1, it is possible to convert a considerable proportion of the original thermal energy into electrical energy while still ensuring that the final temperature T_2 is high enough for the gas to be thermally ionized and therefore highly conducting. However, so far, such favorable conditions have not been achieved in practice. A magnetohydrodynamic generator with an initial gas temperature well in excess of 3,000 – 5,000°K is beyond the reach of present technology, and therefore the temperature of the gas as it enters the magnetic converter cannot be much greater than 3,000°K. At temperatures of this order, the air mixed with the combustion products of the mineral fuel is only weakly ionized and its electrical conductivity is not high enough.

The conductivity could possibly be increased by introducing into the gas jet a small proportion of impurities with low ionization potential, for example, the vapors of alkali metals. The situation is apparently more favorable if a nuclear reactor is employed as the source of thermal energy, since any mixture of gases may then be used as the carrier of thermal energy, provided only that it is not made too radioactive by the nuclear radiation. In particular, one could use helium with small amounts of cesium to increase the electrical conductivity. (The ionization potential of cesium is about 3.8 eV, while the ionization potential of helium is 24.5 eV.) However, even the use of impurities does not lead to plasma jets with resistivities in excess of a few ohm cm, owing to the low electron temperature of the plasma.

A jet of plasma entering the working region, where the magnetic transformation of energy takes place, must necessarily be very dense since it carries a high flux of energy. For example, in the above numerical calculation, the energy flux entering the magnetic converter must exceed 10,000 kVa, and therefore the energy flux density must be greater than 10kVa per cm^2. Since the energy flux density is equal to the product of the amount of energy stored per unit volume and the velocity of the plasma; that is, it is equal to $\frac{1}{2}\rho v^2 \times v$, it follows that $\frac{1}{2}\rho v^3 > 10^{11}$ erg/cm^2 sec. where ρ is the density of the plasma and all the quantities are expressed in cgs units. When $v = 10^5$ cm per sec, the density must exceed 2×10^{-4} g per cm^2. In air, this corresponds to an atomic (and ionic) concentration of about 4×10^{18} particles per cm^3. For comparison, we note that at normal temperatures this would correspond to a pressure of about 100 mm Hg. At such densities, the transfer of thermal energy between the electrons, ions, and neutral atoms in the plasma of the magnetohydrodynamic converter should proceed at a high rate, and this means that the temperature of the electrons cannot be very high.

The electron temperature T_e is determined by the balance between the energy communicated to the electrons by the induced electric field and the energy lost by collisions, mainly with the neutral atoms. The properties of the gas itself play a very important role in this balance. In an atomic gas with a high ionization potential, elastic electron-atom collisions are the most important. In each such collision the electron transmits to the atom only a very small fraction of its kinetic energy, and therefore the total heat transfer from the electron component to the ions and atoms is relatively small. Excitation of atoms should have only a minor effect on the energy balance, since most of the energy lost by the electrons in inelastic collisions is eventually returned as a result of the strong absorption of the radiation by the gas itself. It may therefore be supposed that the electron temperature in a jet of ionized atomic gas is much higher than T_i and T_0. Under these conditions, the process may become practicable with jet resistivities of the order of 1 ohm cm. In a jet of molecular gas, for example, a mixture of air and combustion products, the electron temperature can hardly be different from the temperature of the neutral component, owing to the very strong inelastic interaction between the electrons and the molecules. Therefore, the conductivity of the jet cannot be very high. It follows that at velocities smaller than 10^5 cm per sec, the plasma jet can travel relatively freely across the magnetic lines of force without dragging them along (frequent collisions lead to displacement of the particles relative to the lines of force). In other words, in this case there should be no appreciable freezing-in of the lines of force into the plasma; that is, the passage of the plasma beam through the magnetic field should not lead to a strong distortion of the field.

The development of magnetohydrodynamic generators is still at a very early stage. There is a lack of important fundamental data upon which the basic design calculation may be founded. In particular, very little is known about the conductivity of plasma under working conditions and the nature of the interaction between plasma beams and the working electrodes. Nevertheless, it seems that the magnetohydrodynamic converter will find its place in technology and will eventually displace conventional machinery. This expectation is based on the fact that the efficiency of conversion of thermal into electrical energy in magnetohydrodynamic generators should, at least in principle, be much higher than in steam and gas turbogenerators.

There is an important difference between the physical problems arising in connection with magnetohydrodynamic conversion of energy and the physical aspects of thermonuclear fusion. In the former case, one is concerned with plasmas at enormous temperatures, while in the other with ordinary low-temperature plasma.

In principle, the magnetohydrodynamic converter is a reversible device. It can convert the kinetic energy of plasma into electrical energy, or it may be used to accelerate plasma with the aid of electrodynamic forces by drawing electrical energy from external sources. In the second case, it becomes an accelerator or injector of plasma and can be used as the basis for a plasma jet engine.[17]

8.3 Plasma Engines

Plasma engines are also among the possible future applications of the physics of plasma. Injectors of this kind have already been discussed in one of the preceding chapters. It is convenient, at this juncture, to return to this topic, which has been so widely discussed in the popular literature.

The more striking applications of plasma engines are, of course, those concerned with long-range cosmic flights. In order to ensure that a spaceship will have the necessary maneuverability and autonomous means of transport, rather than be a ballistic object moving as a result of its inertia under the laws of gravitation, the spaceship must be supplied with adequate sources of energy and with jet engines which could be used to perform complicated maneuvres in space. If the trajectory is such that the ability to maneuvre in space is important, then fuel storage becomes an acute problem. The thrust produced by the jet engine is equal to $m_1 v$, where m_1 is the mass ejected per second and v the velocity of the jet. For a given thrust, the consumption of fuel is inversely proportional to the velocity v. In conventional jet engines, using chemical fuels, the velocity of the jet is of the order of 10^5 cm per sec. For a thrust of only 10 kg, a velocity of 10^5 cm per sec will

[17]These remarks are concerned only with physical principles and are not meant to indicate that the practical design problems of magnetohydrodynamic generators and plasma engines are identical. The two devices are, in fact, quite different.

require the consumption of 100 kg of fuel per day, It is apparent that under these conditions the spaceship will only have limited maneuverability.

The amount of fuel which must be carried on board the spaceship can be reduced by a very large factor if conventional jets are replaced by plasma jets with velocities of the order of 10^7 cm per sec. However, this leads to a considerable increase in the rate of energy consumption, since the power necessary to accelerate the jet is $\frac{1}{2}m_1v^2$, and therefore for a given thrust the fuel consumption is proportional to v. It follows that the application of plasma jets for the control of spaceships will require the development of powerful sources of energy, capable of being carried on board the spaceship. The construction and operation of plasma jet engines is still a matter for conjecture. The simplest kind of jet engine is the coaxial plasma injector illustrated in Fig. 67.

This concludes our brief account of some of the possible applications of plasma processes in the near and more distant future. It is quite clear that other, less fanciful, applications will develop in the course of time and will enable the very varied and interesting properties exhibited by plasma to be used for practical purposes.

Fundamental Constants

Electron charge	$e = 4.8 \cdot 10^{-10}$ esu
Electron mass	$m_e = 9 \cdot 10^{-28}$ g
Proton mass	$m_p = 1.67 \cdot 10^{-24}$ g
Speed of light	$c = 3 \cdot 10^{10}$ cm/sec
Planck's constant	$h = 6.62 \cdot 10^{-27}$ erg sec
Baltzmann constant	$k = 1.38 \cdot 10^{-16}$ erg/degree

Index

ABOUT THE AUTHOR

Lev A. Arzimovich is the Director of the Plasma Physics Division of the Institute for Atomic Energy in Moscow. In this job he has assumed the position of the late Dr. Kurchatov who was, until his death a few years ago, considered one of the world's leading authorities on thermonuclear problems.

Academician Arzimovich is a full member of the Academy of Sciences (U.S.S.R.) and a member of its Presidium. He is the foremost Soviet plasma physicist and one of the acknowledged world authorities in this field.

THIS BOOK WAS SET IN

TIMES ROMAN AND PERPETUA TYPES

BY TRADE COMPOSITION, INC.

IT WAS DESIGNED BY THE STAFF OF

BLAISDELL PUBLISHING COMPANY.